VIGILANCE

The Savvy Woman's Guide to Personal Safety,
Self-Protection Measures, and Countermeasures

VIGILANCE

The Savvy Woman's Guide to Personal Safety,
Self-Protection Measures, and Countermeasures

SHELLEY KLINGERMAN

Niche Pressworks

Indianapolis

Vigilance

Copyright © 2019 by Shelley Klingerman

For permission to reprint portions of this content or bulk purchases, contact info@stilettoagency.com

Published by Niche Pressworks, Indianapolis, IN
http://NichePressworks.com

ISBN: 978-1-9465-33-43-2 Paperback
ISBN: 978-1-9465-33-44-9 eBook

Printed in the United States of America

Dedication

This book is dedicated to the women (and men) who have gotten by with good luck and a guardian angel watching over them, but now are ready to add a layer of good habits and awareness to their everyday safety.

On a personal note, it's dedicated to my kids, whom I would go to any length to protect. However, since I can't always be with them, the next best thing I can do is empower them with knowledge and know-how, and to model behaviors so they can stay safe as they begin to explore this world on their own.

And lastly, the book is dedicated to my incredible husband, who always supports my projects, no matter how big or small. Thank you for always letting me do my thing.

Acknowledgements

I want to thank all of my current and retired law enforcement and military friends who, over the years, have answered the many questions and scenarios I've thrown at them. You are true patriots of this nation and globe.

A big thank you to the executive team at the International Tactical Officers Training Association (ITOTA.us), who were truly valuable when I needed to be connected to other resources or just needed confirmation that my information was accurate.

Thank you to Guy Finley, who gave me the opportunity to validate that this topic and subject matter had relevance and could have impact in the corporate community.

Thank you to team Toccoa Security Consulting for sharing your resources and spending time with me.

And finally, I'm grateful to Chief Paul Cell who gave me confirmation that this topic is important, and that this book has a place in the world to help empower women (and men) to keep themselves safe.

Contents

Foreword

There are too few books today that truly address the safety concerns women face in their daily lives. I commend Shelley Klingerman for using her wealth of knowledge and experience to create a book that will help women identify, prepare for, and react in situations when their well-being is threatened.

In my 40 years in law enforcement, I have come to believe the key to survival is vigilance. The motto Prepare—Prevent—Protect is a modern-day approach that will give women the skill set needed when confronted. Today, we continue to be exposed to violent acts that plague our communities. Sexual assault and other forms of violence against women tend to be the most personal crimes one can experience. Now, more than ever, we need to create workable strategies to help mitigate the chances of becoming a victim. Only when a person feels safe can they be empowered to truly control their life.

I am thrilled that Shelley Klingerman expands the notion that women must empower themselves to combat assault—so that the number of victims decreases and those who were victimized become survivors. We must continue to champion, as Shelley writes, the sense of the warrior—a person who shows great vigor, courage, and aggressiveness when needed. Assault no longer hides in the shadows as the vigilance of empowered women shines light through the power of awareness and proactive management of their safety.

As a certified karate instructor for over 35 years, I have strived to ensure that my students learn practical and effective techniques for real life situations. I find this book serves as the perfect companion to anyone who is engaged in the practice of self-protection. Thank you, Shelley, for giving us a book that is long overdue.

Chief Paul M. Cell
President 2018/2019
International Association of Chiefs of Police

Preface

In Laymoms' Terms

Ten years ago, I never would have imagined that I would set out to produce a documentary about—of all things—school safety, and I really never expected that it would lead to writing a book. But this is what can happen when you follow your passions and feed your desire to learn more, make a difference, and have an impact.

This all started when I took a couple of days off from my full-time corporate job in marketing and communications to help a local organization host an anti-terrorism conference. The conference targeted military, law enforcement, and first responders; I was not the target audience. However, I found what they were talking about fascinating, empowering, and most of all, important.

There was one particular keynote speaker who talked about the Beslan, Russia, school siege and honestly changed an aspect of my life. His message and story were ones that I couldn't forget, and some of the images he showed wouldn't leave my mind's eye. I kept seeing my kids and myself, as many parents were involved in that horrific incident along with their children. I did not want anything like that happening to my kids, my community, or my country.

So, I set out to deliver the message in laymoms' terms. The documentary took me about four years to complete because I was working full-time (with travel); I opened a women's boutique (I'm an entrepreneur at heart); and was teaching yoga. I also had two kids at the time I began, and a third child by the time I was finished.

Over the course of producing the documentary, I met some amazing individuals—from ex-special forces operators to ex-terrorists (seriously) as well as outstanding law enforcement officers and first responders. Some of the most interesting conversations would happen when the camera was turned off.

Before going any further, there is something you should know about me. Deep, deep within me, I am a bad-ass wannabe. I love Jason Bourne, Mission Impossible, James Bond, and all those types of action movies. But I'm also fascinated by, and have a huge respect for, all divisions of our military and our special ops groups. That goes for special units of law enforcement as well (e.g., hostage negotiators, SWAT, CSI, etc.). I have an enormous amount of admiration for individuals who step forward to fight for our country.

While producing the documentary, I had the amazing opportunity to interview many individuals from all of these backgrounds. If you poll my family or friends, they will tell you I ask a lot of questions (don't know why that bothers them?).

I just find people and their stories interesting, so I want to learn more about them. As such, after each of the interviews I did for the documentary, I would end up having an equally long conversation that mainly consisted of me peppering my interviewee with more questions. These questions tended to be more about their tradecraft, and as a bad-ass wannabe, I ate it up. I was fascinated by some of the very simple things these individuals did that always gave them the advantage when avoiding or dealing with a crisis.

Over time, I realized that the common thread among all of these individuals was they were vigilant. And their vigilance was second nature. There were things they just did that were ah-ha moments to me, but to them it was just part of their daily routine. These were not hard things to incorporate; they were basically good, smart habits that became their norm. I started implementing these habits in my daily life, and the result was empowerment.

At the time, I traveled for work, often by myself. As I started to take these tips and habits on the road with me, I began to change the way I carried myself and most definitely changed my level of awareness about the things and people around me.

In all the years I traveled for work, no one ever took the time to arm me with this information. Now, I want to share what I've learned to empower you. I encourage you not only to model these behaviors and habits, but to share this information with your family, friends, and colleagues, so they too can become more vigilant.

Introduction

Be a "Bad Ass"

If you travel for work, on mission trips, study abroad, etc., how many times has someone—anyone—sat you down and given you any information on how to be a more vigilant traveler? If your experience is similar to mine, the answer is likely never.

I traveled for work for years, and no one told me anything. It wasn't until I began working on my documentary project that I had the fortunate opportunity to have conversations with experts on this subject matter. It was in conversations with ex-special ops guys and law enforcement officers that I learned what I could and should be doing to keep myself safe while traveling alone.

These behaviors and habits were by no means hard things to do. It's just that no one had ever told me that making simple changes—where I sit, where I stand, where I look, how I look, etc.—could potentially keep me from being a victim. I could actually be a bad ass. I didn't have to be a wannabe anymore.

You, too, can be a bad ass, savvy, vigilant traveler once you know the information, tradecraft, and tactics I'm going to share. You will decrease your risk of being paralyzed with fear because you don't know *what* to do. You will learn how to recognize, avoid, and act if you have to. You are going to be empowered with knowledge that will teach you how to be alert and safe.

You may find some of the topics to be intimidating, maybe a little scary, or absolutely awful (like an active shooter situation). But I promise you, you will be much better off facing your fears now than in a moment of crisis. My goal is to get you to a point where you have the gravitas and actionable knowledge and tools to get yourself to a safe place.

Your confidence and the air with which you carry yourself will be a deterrent to anyone who thinks you will be an easy victim. Whether you are traveling abroad or domestically, give yourself permission to lose the ladylike ways and be a warrior. That warrior attitude and mindset alone will give you the ability to think on your feet in the moment and act or react as required. By the time you get through this book, my goal is for you to know that you always have options. You will know what you need to practice to remain savvy, and you will have more control over the situation at hand than you once thought.

I look forward to you joining the community of savvy bad-ass women.

Chapter 1

Prepare — Prevent — Protect

*There is no harm in hoping for the best as
long as you're prepared for the worst.*

– STEVEN KING

Looking back on my solo traveling days, I was really lucky and very naïve. I gave entirely too much information about myself to complete strangers (e.g., seatmates on a plane, "nice guys" in the hotel bar, customers, etc.). I was way too trusting and not plugged into my surroundings. Because of that, I unknowingly put myself in a lot of risky situations. I would not want my daughters to behave the way I did; they might not be so lucky.

It's not necessary to rely on luck. And the old adage that "ignorance is bliss" isn't a valid excuse when there are people and resources to help you build your personal security gravitas. Today, women are taking the initiative on many fronts, and your personal security gravitas is going to carry over into many aspects of your daily interactions. Among the skills you will gain are recognizing harmful people, creating clear boundaries, and completely avoiding danger whenever possible.

Times have changed. It's as unfortunate as it is necessary that this book has become a reality. When I was in college, starting to spread my wings, and then when I started to travel for work in the early 1990s, I would have never thought it was necessary to have a discussion—let alone training—on what I should do if someone started shooting in a public place. Or what I should do if a deranged fellow student walked into my classroom with a gun. Or how I should handle a situation where I said "no" to a man, but an unwelcome advance continued.

Back then, I didn't feel I had to be switched on, with my radar scanning at all times, when I was by myself. However, it's no longer an option NOT to take proactive measures to keep yourself safe. We must start teaching and modeling this for our kids—especially for our daughters.

Predators lurk among us every day, looking for and plotting ways to achieve their goals, whatever those may be: sowing violence, redressing petty grievances, or achieving martyrdom. What you want to convey to them is that you aren't going to make it easy for them. You will not make it easy for them to wreak havoc on your life.

I never intended to write a book, just like I had no intention of ever producing a documentary. However, both the documentary and this book came about because of a nagging voice in my head and a feeling in my heart that this information is too important not to share.

Like many of you, I traveled for work for many years—often by myself. And believe me, I was very naïve, very trusting, and ultimately very lucky that nothing bad ever happened to me. There were more than a few times that my small-town, Midwest roots allowed me to get myself into some uncomfortable situations. For the most part, I was able to fumble my way out of them.

Those situations created a very uneasy feeling. They were situations that could have been prevented if I'd known how to avoid them or at least known how to confidently get out of them. The good news is, with a little education and training, you can greatly decrease your odds of finding yourself in one of those uncomfortable moments. With training, you will know how to recognize, avoid, disengage, or de-escalate a situation when you know it's heading in a bad direction.

What most women don't realize is that in a crisis situation, you will revert back to what you were trained to do. But, do you have adequate training? How many times has your company, your spouse, or your dad talked to you about how to handle yourself in various situations that may threaten your safety? If your answer is never, you're not alone.

Women are pretty damn good at multitasking. We do it daily, with kids, careers, volunteer work, hobbies, staying fit, etc. But, when it comes to being vigilant, women could use a little help. We are hardwired to be patient, kind, nurturing, and understanding, but those genuine qualities can also be the same qualities that potentially allow us to be taken advantage of ... until now.

Prepare—Prevent—Protect is the mantra you're going to keep repeating. The majority of what will be covered in this book is about preparation. I'll address daily situations that women find themselves in and examine how you can be better prepared in the event something doesn't go as expected—you're approached by an unwelcome person, you're in an uncomfortable conversation, you sense you're being followed, or an all-out crisis breaks out. *Preparing* and being able to read these scenarios before they escalate can *prevent* something bad from happening, ultimately *protecting* you.

I'm going to keep repeating this, because it's important to truly understand—in a crisis situation, you will revert back to what you were trained to do. What happens when you weren't trained to do anything? What do you do then? Stop and think about that.

Take a minute and create this scenario in your head: You've just landed at the airport, grabbed a taxi, and given the driver the address, knowing the general direction of your destination. Your driver begins to head to your destination, but then starts making turns that you know are in the opposite direction. You start going through some rough parts of town, and the population is getting sparser. Your heart starts to race; your mind starts to run various scenarios of what this driver might be up to. However, you sit there, becoming more and more nervous, because you don't know what to do. THAT is why we are here—to learn how to avoid that horrible feeling of helplessness. There ARE things you can do to put yourself in a position of power, and that is what you're going to learn.

Prepare

Self-confident people will lead and thrive in a crisis situation. Self-confidence favors composure over panic and response over paralysis. However, overconfidence can be a liability and result in a disregard for danger. You want to strike a balance between being overconfident and empowered. That empowerment comes from knowledge.

We've all heard the saying, "Knowledge is power." However, knowledge is not power unless you couple it with action. This is absolutely true when it comes to being vigilant. I'll talk more about what it means to be vigilant in the next chapter. Being empowered is knowing what to do in a crisis situation and can make the difference between being a victim or a survivor.

As you gain knowledge and learn how and when to engage or disengage, you will not be as likely to become someone's prey, and you will be empowered to handle situations as they present themselves. You will adopt situational awareness in your daily life, reducing your likelihood of becoming a victim. You will accomplish this by replacing overreaction and hypersensitivity with thought and reasoning skills. By the end of the book, I hope you are well on your way to developing a warrior mindset.

By definition, a warrior is a person who shows or has shown great vigor, courage, or aggressiveness. As Keith Sippman writes, a 'warrior mindset' integrate "the psychological with the physical and tactical training to add a dimension that is often overlooked, but necessary to achieve maximum performance of a skill."[1]

When talking about this topic with a Navy SEAL friend of mine, I asked him what having a warrior mindset meant to

---

[1]   Sipmann, Keith. "Warrior Mindset: Train Your Brain • The Havok Journal." *The Havok Journal*, 6 Mar. 2018, havokjournal.com/culture/warrior-mindset-train-your-brain/.

him. He said it was having the mental and physical training to make a decision to act when you only have a split second to make a decision.

He asked me, "How many times have you actually punched someone in the face?" The quick answer was many ... in my head—especially around a conference table during a business meeting (I'm guessing you can relate). But those don't count. In reality, I had to honestly say I have never punched anyone in the face on purpose and with force. He said, "Exactly. And what makes you think you'll be able to if you haven't conditioned yourself and gotten past your first resistance to do it?"

He went on to explain that if you expect yourself to do something in a crisis moment, you have to train your brain to allow you to do so. It has to be familiar and comfortable so that you don't hesitate. If that is what you need to do to keep yourself from being a victim, that's what you have to do.

The way to do it is to visualize yourself in that situation, get your adrenaline pumping, and then practice doing it. I mean, physically practice it with a punching bag (for extra motivation, you can tape a familiar or unfamiliar face on it as a target). In order to be able to execute, you not only need to know what to do, but you also need to practice by physically performing some of these techniques. And doing them under stress is the absolute best way to practice.

A great way to get practice and experience what your body will do under stress is to compete—or take a class where sparring is part of the training. I used to take a Brazilian Jiu Jitsu/Jeet Kune Do class. Brazilian Jiu Jitsu is a martial arts and combat sport system that focuses on grappling with particular emphasis on ground fighting. Jeet Kune Do (JKD) trains various fighting styles including knife sparing, boxing, and other drills. It literally means "the way of intercepting the fist".

I was often the only female in class. When I had to spar with the instructor or other classmates, my heart would start racing, my breathing would become shallow, and I would start shaking. These were 90 second rounds that felt like 5 minutes, but there was no "stopping" before the 90 seconds were up.

If you got clocked within the first few seconds and put your hands down, exposing your face, you can bet you'd get clocked again. But after a few times, you learned how to maintain your concentration and keep your hands in front of your face. As soon as the round was over, I had such a sense of relief—I realized I survived! Next to being involved in a real situation, competition is a great way to reproduce the stress response.

In addition to Jiu Jitsu studios, some other great places to look for classes where you can get this type of hands-on experience include boxing gyms and the YMCA. Local churches also sometimes offer personal protection classes. If nothing else, take the lead and reach out to one of these places and organize a class on your own. Local or state law enforcement agencies often have officers who will lead classes. Ex-military personnel are also ideal instructors.

You can influence what happens to you by taking more responsibility for your own safety. By developing a warrior mindset, you become energetically engaged. This type of mindset has a lot to do with being adaptive and creatively solving problems.

Preparation and believing that you can do whatever it takes in the moment are essential for a successful warrior mindset, impacting how you behave in stressful situations and how you will react. You also must be open to learning new things and continue to expand your knowledge base.

If you are motivated to be safe, it is more likely you will behave in a way that protects you, and you will continue to learn, practice, and visualize yourself in various situations. Don't be overwhelmed or intimidated by the thought of this. Simply use free moments—at stoplights, on plane flights, or during alone time in coffee shops or at your desk—to set a scenario in your head and run through your choices for how to react.

The benefit of this is that you will give yourself a lot of options for quickly solving a problem. This will improve your chances of acting in the moment—without hesitation—and will give you confidence, knowing that you do have options, and you should act, rather than do nothing.

Think of someone you feel exhibits a warrior mindset. Maybe it's one of our military or law enforcement leaders. Perhaps it's someone who had an experience that required them to dig deep to ensure their survival. Or it might be someone who has written a book after a tragic incident. Study these people; learn from them. Model their behavior. Listen to their experiences.

They all can provide examples of things you can continuously be doing to expand your base of knowledge. You never know when one of these small nuggets of information may be the one that you will need to go to in a time of crisis. How many times have you seen a news story where the person referred to doing something they saw on TV? It doesn't matter where you get the info, as long as you process it, break it down, and lock it in.

Prevent

Prevention is something we should all be aware of and practice while we have the gift of time on our side. A key element to staying safe is, when at all possible, prevention. We need to avoid getting into a risky situation in the first place. That means learning to recognize signs of something getting ready to go down, noticing unusual activity in familiar situations, noting a person displaying strange or out-of-the-ordinary behavior, etc.

Just like your health, when it comes to your safety, prevention is always the best option. Your intuition is one of the best tools for prevention; it's a gift that's been given to you. Notice and trust those valuable feelings that you get. Just as all your feelings play an important role in your life (anger, fear, happiness, sadness, etc.), your intuition is invaluable when it comes to signaling you to stay out of harm's way.

As Carlin Flora writes in *Psychology Today*, psychologists believe that "intuition is a mental matching game. The brain takes in a situation, does a very quick search of its files, and then finds its best analogue among the stored sprawl of memories and knowledge. Based on that analogy, you ascribe meaning to the situation in front of you."[2] This is similar to a doctor making a diagnosis after considering a patient's symptoms.

---

[2]   Flora, Carlin. "Gut Almighty." 1 May 2007, *Psychology Today*, www.psychologytoday.com/us/articles/200705/gut-almighty.

It turns out there's a reason people say, "I feel it in my gut." There are millions of nerve cells in your gut, which researchers believe almost makes it have a mind of its own. The signals are coming from your brain, but the nerve cells help you feel it in your gut. These feelings play a part in your emotion and intuition.

Flora goes on to explain that experts describe intuition as "almost immediate situational understanding," as opposed to "immediate knowledge."[3] Our understanding of the situation is filled with emotion—we feel it. Individuals who don't rely on their intuition are often cognitively paralyzed when confronted with a situation. Their ability to think and quickly make decisions is severely limited. That's why continuously making experiential and knowledge-based deposits in your brain can come back to serve you in a time of need.

Reflect on how many times someone has been telling you a story about something bad that happened to them, and they say, "I had a feeling." But, they ignored it. Don't ignore your gut.

Protect

Your ultimate protection will come from putting in the time to empower yourself with tools and knowledge and allowing yourself to stay calm. Knowing that you have options, in almost any situation, helps prevent panic.

You'll learn to become innovative when it comes to being vigilant and protecting yourself. You'll learn to look at everyday

---

[3] Ibid

objects and see something completely different. Who said a small bottle of hand sanitizer can't become a means to protect yourself? It most certainly can when it's squirted into someone's eyes.

It's natural to panic when you think you have no control, but you almost always do. Training yourself to apply innovation when it comes to personal protection will put you at an advantage. My goal is to guide you to a place where you will not be paralyzed with fear in any situation. Positive action will come from your mental preparation.

So, we've learned that, in addition to preparation, simply knowing what to look for—recognizing and avoiding a situation—is the key to prevention or avoidance. And knowing how to prevent something from happening is the best form of protection. Why walk right into a hornet's nest if you can go around it? When you've finished this book, your ability to protect yourself is going to increase greatly.

Chapter 2

What is Vigilance?

Better a thousand times careful than once dead.

– PROVERB

My friend Paul shared a story with me about a time his dad was coming out of a meeting late at night in a not-so-great neighborhood. As he approached his car, he noticed a number of older teenagers, sitting on his car hanging out.

Knowing it was going to be uncomfortable to ask them to get off his car, he stayed calm and collected, and quickly thought on his feet. He looked up at the building along the side of his car and started waving and yelling, "Yeah, I see you! I'll call you tomorrow!" He said this while pointing up and behind the teens. He kept smiling and nodding as if he were signaling a friend standing in the window. However, he wasn't actually talking to anyone.

He did this with the hope that if the group of teenagers had plans to jump or mug him, they now thought there would be witnesses—the "people" in the building above. It worked. As Paul's dad approached his car, the teens got off and moved on without incident.

Vigilance is a word that was used a lot around 9/11 and has had another spike in use over the last few years as lone wolf terrorist attacks have increased around the world. But what does it mean when someone says, "Remain vigilant"? What should you actually do? Being attentive and vigilant are components of situational awareness—being tuned in to your surroundings.

Situational awareness means being aware of what is happening around you, and understanding how information, events, and one's own actions will impact the situation, both immediately and in the near future.

Vigilance is defined as the action of keeping careful watch for possible danger or difficulties.

When you're by yourself, regardless of whether you're on a business trip abroad or simply going to the gym or shopping center in your own neighborhood, your behavior should be the same. Perhaps you don't need the exact same level of awareness because your regular routes are familiar, but you still need to be attentive enough to know if something is different or out of place.

Maybe you go to the gym early in the morning and have a favorite parking spot because it's close to the door. But one morning, you notice there is someone sitting in their car right next to your spot. You've applied vigilance. You elect to park in a spot further away that morning to create distance between yourself and the person in the car. Yes, they may be a fine individual— or they may not be. But, by taking the prevention approach we talked about, you can avoid the possibility of placing yourself in danger altogether.

A simple decision like that can be a situational awareness moment—in just a second, you note that perhaps, for today, you need to change your routine. Unfortunately, there are people who are so programmed in their habits and actions that they may not even notice the need to make a different decision when something doesn't seem right.

Awareness

Just by practicing simple awareness, you can change your personal risk profile immediately. It's all about finding the right level of situational awareness and maintaining an appropriate level of vigilance.

I realize the technical definition of vigilance may sound very basic and simple, and it really is. Perhaps you think to yourself, "I'm totally aware of what's going on around me all the time." Really? What about when you're checking your phone (which we do approximately 75 times a day)? Or worse, checking your phone while walking? Perhaps you've seen the videos of people looking at their phone while walking and literally falling into a fountain or walking off a curb into traffic. And everyone sits in coffee shops or other public places, head down, on their phone. Constantly looking down—instead of looking around—is a bad habit that makes you very vulnerable.

The next time you find yourself texting and walking ... stop! Notice (and admit) that you're doing it and stop. In fact, each time you find yourself doing it, verbally say, "Stop." Do this until you undo the habit. It will take some time and effort because it's so ingrained in us that we usually don't even realize we're doing it.

Of course, the issue isn't really with checking your phone— it's the fact that a predator loves to find an easy target. They love to identify someone who's not paying a bit of attention to what's going on around them. Social media makes a predator's job easier, because it sucks you into a state of disengagement from your surroundings. If you exhibit signs that you're "switched on," you're not going to be seen as an easy target, and you can avoid danger.

Another important part of vigilance is regularly scanning your surroundings and taking note of what's going on around you. All you have to do is look and make mental notes. Being proactive about scanning your surroundings when in train stations, airports, malls, large venues, parking lots, etc. is a great habit to get into. Think about the James Bond movies when Bond is sitting in a restaurant. He can be deep in conversation and looking straight ahead but can still tell you everything that's going on around the room.

You certainly don't need to have that skill level to be effective, but simply looking around and noticing things will automatically increase your level of vigilance. Think about doing that—all the time. Be in the moment and take notice.

This simple action allows you to think quickly and gives you the opportunity to see something that may be getting ready to unfold. A few extra seconds of identifying a crisis gives you time to analyze and start taking action. It allows your OODA (pronounced oo-da) Loop to kick in and guide your actions in the moment.

OODA Loop

We each use OODA Loop processing countless times every day, probably without even knowing it. Essentially, it's how we approach the decision-making. An OODA Loop organizes decisions into four steps—Observe, Orient, Decide, and Act.

If things are familiar and going along as expected, we may not even notice that we're following these steps. Think about a task you complete on a daily basis, like driving to work. You probably get in your car, drive the same way to work every day, and don't even think about it. You may be thinking about dinner plans or upcoming meetings while still making every turn and arriving at work as expected.

This happens so seamlessly because the OODA Loop worked. You completed the observation, orientation, and decision process during your first few drives to work. Now, you can complete the action without much thought or energy (or input from the other steps).

It's when something unexpected occurs that the OODA Loop process is particularly effective, because it provides a structure for how to respond in stressful situations, which results in faster reaction times.

The OODA Loop concept was developed by US Air Force Colonel John Boyd who created the strategy for fighter pilots who need to make life-and-death decisions quickly while juggling multiple other tasks. The OODA approach improves reaction times in stressful or unknown situations by setting specific steps to follow—Observe, Orient, Decide, and Act. This structured approach effectively conditions your mind and body to react quickly without having to think about it, which guarantees speedier response times.

These are all reasons OODA is used extensively in the military. However, its effectiveness and usefulness as a decision-making tool make it popular in other fields as well, including self-defense training, business, sports, and medicine. In these fields, quick decision-making capabilities give you an enormous advantage.

While many people respond to stressful situations by making a move and waiting to see what happens, OODA encourages rapid-fire responses based on the specific situation and your own capabilities. Your quick reaction keeps the initiative on your side. Let's look at how this works.

Observe

The first step during any stressful event involves observing what is happening and taking in as much information as possible about the situation. At this point, it's most important that you gather data and less important that it makes sense. Try to be present and available to everything that is happening.

Orient

The next step requires making sense of all the information you have about a situation in relation to your own perspective, experience, and capabilities. In this sense, you're mentally and physically orienting yourself in the situation and filtering all your observations into actionable items.

Effectively orienting yourself requires thinking and looking at the data, thinking through possible actions, and coming up with a plan (or multiple plans). It's essential to stay calm and focused at this phase so you can think clearly about what's happening and prepare for the next step. At the end of this phase, you should have one or more options.

Decide

At this point, you need to decide what to do in response to the threat or situation. This step relies on what you've determined from the first two phases. You are likely to have multiple options, but you need to select the one with the best possible outcome based not only on the situation, but also your own capabilities and position. You want a decision that says, "if I take this action, then *this* outcome (which is the one I want) will likely happen."[4]

Act

Now, you act and implement your decision. It's important, at this point, to remember that this is a loop. The action you take shouldn't be thought of as crossing the finish line. Instead, it's better to view it as testing your hypothesis (decision).

---

[4]   Sturm, Mike. "The OODA Loop: A Tool for Better Decision-Making – Personal Growth – Medium." *Medium.com*, Medium, 11 Mar. 2017, medium.

Since it is a loop, you may need to continue the process by looping back to the beginning. At this point, you start over again by observing, orienting, and deciding if you need to take a different action.

Viewing your actions as tests for your decisions should help keep the process in perspective and allow you to learn and adapt based on the experience.

The Loop

Once you have acted on your decision, you continue the loop until either the situation is resolved, or you need to readjust your approach. If you need to take a different approach, simply restart the loop.

Training

Since the OODA loop is a purely mental thing, it is a difficult skill set to develop. Training is best accomplished by playing rapid "what if" games and then practicing. This is a great application of visualization—mentally placing yourself in a situation and then seeing yourself, in your mind's eye, moving through the OODA steps and getting to safety.

One way to train your brain is to take headlines from the news and think through what you would do in those situations, specifically using the OODA approach. The objective is to review

com/personal-growth/the-ooda-loop-a-tool-for-better-decision-making-that-youre-already-using-ca24a3fa8c5c.

in your mind how you would react to the actual event. Doing this challenge prepares (or orients) you for future stressful situations so that you are less surprised or taken off guard when you encounter the unexpected. In fact, you are mentally preparing yourself to act when the unforeseen occurs.

Speed

Rehearsing scenarios can help make OODA looping second nature, which improves reaction times. The speed at which you get through the loop can give you an edge. The objective is to get through the loop faster than your adversary. In an ideal situation, you react to a threat before your attacker has a chance to enter his loop, disrupting his plan. If not, the attacker has time to react; then you have to get inside his loop. This means that you need to be performing your loop faster than he can perform his. That's why practice and visualization are so important, so response actions are second nature and you can gain an advantage through speed.

Attitude

One of the most serious obstacles to personal safety is an attitude of complacency—the "It won't happen to me" attitude. The more practical attitude to is, "If it's going to happen to me, I'm going to be prepared." If you adopt this attitude and imagine yourself in everyday situations (as well as those you may experience while traveling), you can begin to visualize what you should do if that situation does unfold. Having the right attitude allows you to address any vulnerability head on.

As mentioned, visualization is an important preparation step. If you have trained yourself on this process, you are likely to be moving toward safety before the trouble even begins. You want your OODA to kick in. An important factor in all of this is staying calm, which is much easier said than done of course, but it can be done.

When you remain calm, a major advantage you'll have is that you will be in a much better position to think your way out of a bad situation. Most people, when faced with crisis or adversity, tend to panic. They completely come unglued and freeze with fear. You are not going to do that because you know you have options. There are always options. Sometimes they may not be ideal, easy, or obvious options, but just knowing you can always do something becomes empowering. In reality, doing nothing is also an option—but it's most likely not the best one.

You are less likely to stay calm if you haven't invested time in putting yourself in the mindset of a crisis scenario and visualizing yourself getting through it. Keep in mind, sometimes the things we visualize ourselves doing are much easier in our virtual world than they will be in real life. For instance, if I do a visualization exercise where I'm in my house with my children and a fire breaks out, in my head, I grab my kids and carry them out of the burning house. In reality, I have never tried to do it and might not actually be able to carry them. But the visualization is still valuable because I've thought about what we need to do should we ever have a fire.

Warrior Mindset

When it comes to building your warrior mindset, make sure you physically try to do the things you are visualizing yourself doing.

You don't want to create a false expectation that you're able to perform a task that you physically can't.

When practicing vigilance, don't disregard your intuition, that gut feeling you get about something that often turns out to be right. Intuition is the ability to understand something instinctively, without the need for conscious reasoning. We utilize our intuition when we are in an unfamiliar situation (stressful or non-stressful), and we need to make a decision.

Your intuition will work better when you use it along with common sense and knowledge. Building your knowledge should be an ongoing task, and you're doing it right now by reading this book. You're depositing knowledge, tips, tactics, and information in your brain to have on hand and pull from in those times requiring quick decisions.

It's important to learn to trust intuition, especially in high-stress situations, because it's in those scenarios where seconds count. That's when the saying "Trust your intuition" is most important.

Trusting your intuition is also part of being vigilant as it relates to surveillance detection—being able to sense that someone (or a group) is paying close attention to your moves, conversations, and activities. It might be as simple as catching someone's eyes or noticing that feeling of having eyes on you.

Being able to pick up on subtle surveillance, acknowledging it, and making a decision to do something eliminates that element of surprise by the predator. Predators rely heavily on the element of surprise; however, you are not going to allow it. The simple act of identifying the surveillance may be able to help you prevent something from happening. You can often avoid trouble simply by being plugged in and paying attention. It doesn't take a lot of skill but can be incredibly effective.

The difference between confidence and overconfidence is vigilance. Being overconfident can lead to complacency—letting your guard down and adopting the dangerous, "It's not going to happen to me" mindset. Conversely, lacking confidence can result in constantly anticipating that something bad will inevitably happen, causing you to overreact. But real confidence, founded on preparation, is a great advantage; it results in empowerment. In the end, commonsense precautionary measures can be taken to reduce the likelihood of being a victim.

Chapter 3

Personal Preparation

No matter what type of crime occurs, it's common to feel helpless when one becomes the victim. Remember: In a crisis situation, you will revert back to what you were trained to do. This means that proper preparation is important.

There are three things that must be in place in order for a crime to be committed—a target, desire, and opportunity.

- A **target** is the object of a predator's desire.
- **Desire** is what motivates a perpetrator to commit a crime.
- **Opportunity** is the alignment of circumstances in which a crime can be committed.

Without all three of these elements, a crime will probably not be committed. Knowing this gives you the power to prevent a crime from happening to you. Don't be a target (or at least don't be an easy target). Recognize when you are placing yourself into an opportunistic situation for a predator. The desire of a predator is something that you will likely not be able to change. But your goal is to make it hard to bring their trifecta together around you.

Preparedness Traits

There are some character traits that are important to have as a strong foundation on which to continue building your preparedness skills. All these traits relate to how you present yourself.

Determination – having a firm purpose; willingness to work hard toward a goal

Courage – the ability to face obstacles, danger, and hard decisions; ability to do something which frightens you

Self-control – being in command of your feelings, actions, behaviors

Bravery – fearless or courageous behavior or character

Attitude – individuality and self-confidence, as manifested by behavior or appearance; how you choose to conduct yourself

Confidence – trusting and believing in your own abilities

Initiative – ability to begin a plan or task and follow it through energetically

Developing all these traits translates into empowerment.

A good place to begin is with self-confidence. Confidence helps you better evaluate your security intelligence—measuring how well you know your strengths and limitations, and how well you can apply your skills and awareness in a threatening situation.

The above traits also come into play when finding your appropriate level of situational awareness. If you think about it, on a daily basis, there are various levels of situational awareness needed, depending on where you are and what you are doing.

Now that you are becoming more vigilant, you may start noticing the unsuspecting, checked-out people around you. Categorize them into one of the following groups or make up some states of awareness terms of your own.

Comatose – completely tuned out to what's going on; not looking around, eyes glazed over, zombie-like behavior. This is not how you want to go about your day. This behavior makes you completely vulnerable and susceptible to being caught off guard.

Tuned out – going about your business, looking at your phone, deep in thought without attention to what's going on around you. You may look up if you hear something, but you're not going to pick up on it a moment before it happens.

Relaxed awareness – taking note of things that are normal as you go through the day but noticing when something is out of the ordinary and pausing long enough to determine if you should act. This is the ideal daily state to be in.

Focused – going through your day constantly looking around, taking note of everything and everyone. This is a good state to step up to when traveling, especially in unfamiliar places, or if you suddenly sense that something is not right. But it might not be necessary for your day-to-day routine.

High alert – this is a state of paranoia that really isn't productive. Staying in a state of high alert triggers a fight-or-flight reaction in our brain, which dumps adrenaline into our system. This unnecessary stress isn't good for our health.

The Fight-or-Flight Response

When we encounter a situation that makes us feel threatened, our mind and body process what's going in several different stages. These stages impact how we respond. If you become familiar with these stages and learn how they may affect you, you'll better understand why your body is reacting the way it is, which can help minimize the fear of the unknown. This allows you to focus your attention on surviving.

In an article in *Fight Times*, Warren Breckenridge explains that "the three specific mental states that a person goes through when facing a threat are: Threat Anxiety, Survival Stress, and Combat Stress.[5]

The initial stage, threat anxiety, occurs at the first hint that there might be danger. It's unknown if the cause is simply a fear of the unknown, or a sense that injury or death may occur. But the result is a signal to the sympathetic nervous system to release the hormones epinephrine (also known as adrenaline) and norepinephrine into our system. This triggers the autonomic nervous system's fight-or-flight decision—in the interest of self-preservation, do you stay and fight, or do you flee?

As a result of the body's chemical response to threat anxiety, we then enter the second stage, survival stress. The flood of hormones sets off multiple physical reactions—our blood pressure and heart rate increase, our pupils become dilated, and

---

[5]   Breckenridge, Warren. "Fight or Flight - The Three Stages." *Fight Times Magazine*, 13 Sept. 2009, magazine.fighttimes.com/fight-or-flight-the-three-stages/.

our digestive system slows down. And, in order to divert blood flow to our brain, organs, and muscles, the blood vessels in our extremities start to constrict.

This is a primal defense mechanism, but the body's reaction is the same today. And the resulting physical effects are sometimes unexpected. For example, as the blood flow is diverted from your extremities, your hands might begin to feel numb. Additionally, the rush of adrenaline that is now being pumped through your body can make you feel jittery, affecting both fine and complex motor skills.

The result is that seemingly simple things (like dialing a number on your cell phone or handling a weapon) can become very difficult. Other things you may experience include tunnel vision, loss of depth perception, inability to focus, loss of memory, and an inability to process information.

This may be why when people are questioned after a crisis situation, they frequently can't recall anything other than the specific threat they encountered. Other details, like witnesses, conversations, etc. have not been retained, as the body focused all its attention on survival.

Breckenridge describes the final stage, combat stress, as when "the body is affected by what is referred to as backlash. Once the threat has diminished the parasympathetic nervous system is reactivated. The PNS allows the body to rest and conserve energy. Blood pressure lowers, the heart slows, and digestion starts again."[6] As with survival stress, there are

---

[6]   Ibid.

physical responses during the combat stress stage. When the blood starts to flow back into your extremities, your hands may begin to shake, and any open wounds will start to bleed more, requiring immediate attention.

The above is not an all-inclusive list of reactions during these threat stages—a variety of other side effects may also occur. But understanding that these responses are normal—a primitive, natural response to danger—can help to minimize fears that may be caused by any unexpected responses from your own body.

It's important, yet difficult, to recreate adrenaline effects when trying to train and prepare to respond in high-stress situations. That's why you'll see police and the military train with high-sensory drills—bright flashing lights, noise pumped in, use of blank ammunition to mimic gunfire, etc. The idea is to do as much as they can to stimulate the body's senses, so they can train to react in chaotic situations, with tunnel vision effects, decreased fine motor skills, increased heart rate, etc.

These drills help participants learn how their body reacts to stressful situations, so they aren't distracted by their body's reactions when they are facing a real threat. Some of the other physical effects of the fight-or-flight response include:

Cool pale skin: As mentioned above, blood flow is diverted from the extremities, which allows it to be used to enhance the performance of the brain, eyes, ears, nose, arms, legs, and shoulders. This is what helps us to think quickly and run and fight. We are also better able to identify threats because our ability to hear, see, and smell things is improved. Directing blood away from our skin also helps minimize any bleeding from cuts and scrapes.

Dry mouth: When our digestive system slows down in response to a threat, the production of gastric juices and saliva is diminished. Our body knows that it's more important to survive than to metabolize food. This reaction makes our mouth to feel dry and may also cause an upset stomach.

Sweating: Both fighting and fleeing may cause an increase in body temperature. To offset that anticipated reaction, the body begins to sweat as soon as it feels stressed. This is aptly named "stress sweat" and comes from different glands than the sweat that comes from vigorous exercise.

Shaking: Shaking is a physical way for our muscles to expel stress. While in a threatening or scary situation (or coming out of one), where our bodies have been physically tense, shaking is an expected effect.

Instincts and Intuition

A couple of other God-given traits are our instinct and intuition. Both are valuable when it comes to keeping you safe.

Instinct is your natural, innate response to certain stimuli that stems from the subconscious. You cover your face or duck when someone pretends to throw something at you.

Intuition was discussed in detail in earlier parts of this book. Author Cristen Rogers says that intuition is "the North Star of the human soul—an ever-present inner guide to help us navigate the different landscapes of life."[7]

---

[7]   Rodgers, Cristen. "The Difference Between Intuition and Instinct." *Exemplore*, Exemplore, 5 Apr. 2017, exemplore.com/misc/The-Difference-Between-

She goes on to explain the difference between instinct and intuition, and how to tell them apart. "Whereas instinct speaks in terms of resistance, intuition speaks in terms of flow. Intuition will urge you to go this way, do this thing, or approach that person. If something isn't right for you, intuition won't push against it. Instead, it will simply redirect you towards something else." But instinct, Rogers says, "pushes back. It resists, fears, or judges what you perceive as wrong rather than beckoning you toward what's right."[8]

Both are really important, and you need both to build self-trust. I'm sure you've heard news stories about Good Samaritans who noticed that something seemed out of place, or they had a feeling that something wasn't right. They reported it and stopped some kind of bad event from happening.

This is where you need to be, acknowledging and trusting the signals that your psyche is giving off. Many people want to ignore these signs because they don't want to take the time to listen to them, or they don't want to be a burden to law enforcement (the "What if I'm wrong" concern). Law enforcement actually appreciates you burdening them with tips; your piece of information might complete a case they've been trying to solve, validate something they had an eye on, or bring to their attention something they should look into. They would much prefer to get more information than not enough.

Intuition-and-Instinct.

[8]   Ibid.

What you don't want to do is to ignore these signs and signals (or proceed to act against them), getting yourself into a situation that could have been avoided. You may find yourself in situations where all you have are your instincts and intuition to keep you safe—hopefully that will lead to complete avoidance. Paying attention to those inner warnings can prevent you from being close when something bad goes down, because you "got the feeling" and trusted yourself to act.

Safe Behaviors

Before you even get to the stage of relying on instinct and intuition, though, your personal behaviors can greatly impact your safety. Predators are looking for someone that will be easy to subdue, move, and attack. Giving clear signals that you are aware, clued in, and ready to respond makes you less likely to be chosen as a victim. When walking, it's important to exude confidence.

From a body language perspective, there are several things you can do to clearly indicate confidence:

- **Keep your head up and your eyes scanning:** This signals awareness and says that you know what's going on around you.

- **Walk with intention:** This doesn't mean run or even walk quickly, it just means to be deliberate with your steps and make it clear that you know where you're going. Studies show that predators are more likely to pick a victim that has an uneven gait than one who walks evenly and with purpose.

- **Keep your face out of your phone and don't stop to search through your bag or purse:** Not only do these actions make you less aware of what's happening around you, they also put you in a "low power" body position, where you are folded in on yourself. That can be read as lacking confidence and can make you a more likely target.

- **Straighten your spine and walk tall:** To a predator, the more confidence you exude, the more of problem you might be as a victim, so they might think twice about attacking you.

- **Use your voice:** Your voice is powerful. If you feel like someone is following you or is standing too close, addressing them directly with a clear, strong command to get back or stay away can be alarming enough to make them leave you alone. A noisy victim makes their job harder, so the more vocal you are about their behavior, the less they want to deal with you.

- **Keep your hands visible and free:** If you can readily fight back, you are a less attractive victim. Having your hands free and visible lets a potential attacker know that you are able and ready to engage in a fight if needed. Try not to be bogged down with bags or have things in your hands, other than a set of keys.

- **Be aware of your space and use the "Find your nearest exit" strategy:** Avoid getting into spaces where you could be easily trapped or subdued, and don't go anywhere with a single in/out route if it can be avoided. A predator is looking for opportunity to get the upper hand, and trapping you is ideal. Don't give them the chance to use the environment or space you are in against you.

These traits and behaviors should become your personal protocol. These are all things that you can learn to do naturally. When leaving a building, you scan the surroundings before you start walking. You will pull your shoulders back, keep your head up, look around (not down at your phone), and walk with purpose. As you pass people, make brief eye contact. No need to stare them down; just lock eyes in a glance of acknowledgment. Doing these simple things makes you much more vigilant than 80% of the people around you.

Next time you're leaving a business meeting and walking to your car, instead of pulling your phone out, you're going to keep your phone put away and look around. You'll be scanning your surroundings, noting anything that catches your attention, while keeping your head up and body language strong.

Your personal protocol is also going to help you do something that is very important, and that is to blend in. People often make themselves a target with their own behavior. They make themselves stand out like a sore thumb, which can send the message to a predator that the individual is in an unfamiliar place and that puts them at a disadvantage. By exhibiting confidence, you naturally make adjustments to your personal behavior in order to blend in.

If you travel to a foreign country (or any area that is different from what you're used to), you need to note how people are carrying themselves. If you're in another country and the pace of walking is brisk, make sure you're keeping pace. Likewise, if you come from a big city where you're used to barreling your way through the streets, but are in a place where they walk slower, then slow down. It sounds almost remedial to even say that, but without making a conscious effort to go with the flow, you will revert back to your natural pace of walking.

Take a moment to visualize these two scenarios:

Set a scene in your head where the streets are bustling, and you're walking at your normal, leisurely pace with people walking around you from both sides. Note in your mind's eye how you might stand out.

Next, see yourself walking faster than everyone around you, weaving in and out between people. You may actually be running late and need to speed up, but to someone who's looking for something that stands out, you'll be drawing unwanted attention to yourself. One might assume that if you're in a hurry, you're likely not paying close attention to your surroundings.

In both scenarios, you're not in the moment and might be so preoccupied you don't notice what's going on around you. As routine as these behaviors are, they are enough to call attention to yourself. You may not be thinking a thing about it, but to someone who's specifically looking for this behavior, you've made their job much easier.

Emotional Intelligence

Your situational awareness and personal protocol are going to give you the ability to make on-the-fly adjustments to your behavior, so you can recognize how to blend into whatever environment you're in. This idea is very similar to blending into a business or social setting, by mirroring the others in the room and giving off power and confidence signals.

All of this is part of emotional intelligence, or EQ. This is the idea that an ability to understand and manage emotions greatly increases our chances of success. After the concept of an emotional intelligence quotient (EQ) was first proposed in the 1980s, it quickly took off and went on to greatly influence the way people think about emotions and human behavior. Many aspects of EQ are very relevant to our personal protection, including self-awareness, self-management, and social awareness. When it comes to keeping yourself safe, emotional intelligence is just as important as your IQ—maybe even more important.

Your emotional intelligence will allow you to review your security competence, which is comprised of knowledge, travel skills, and an attitude that demonstrates a healthy and realistic respect for various threats to your safety and security. Be very proud of the fact that by reading this book, you are making great strides toward acknowledging and realizing "it" can happen to you, and you are preparing to make sure it doesn't.

A good protocol to have in place is one that addresses communication. Get in the habit of letting people know your travel schedule, especially when you're out of town. When I traveled a lot for work, I remember there were a few trips where the time difference was such that I didn't check in with my husband regularly. There were a couple of times when I didn't talk to him for days.

Looking back, that was really irresponsible on my part, as he was the one person I normally talked to while on business. Had something happened, and I disappeared, he most likely would have been the last person I spoke with. This predated "Find my Phone" and all the other tracking types of technology we have today. My last phone call check-in would have provided a location to start searching for me. But, when I let days pass without calls to him, it would have made it much more difficult to figure out my last whereabouts.

Now that so many communication apps are available, download one that allows domestic and international texting and calling. WhatsApp and WeChat are two examples; however, there are others that do the same thing. Get in a routine of touching base on a regular basis and be intentional about sharing your itinerary with a family member, friend, or colleague.

Use the available technology to let trusted people see your location. And if you're traveling with a business colleague (or anyone, for that matter), discuss a plan for what to do if you're separated for some unexpected reason. If a natural disaster, fire, or attack of some kind occurs, have a place to physically meet up. Understand that most likely, cell towers will be jammed, so you won't be able to depend solely on cell phones.

Typically, fear, denial, excitement, lack of awareness, and lack of preparation prevents women, in particular, from properly planning their travel. However, your honed emotional intelligence is now going to make sure that the first thing you do is weigh the risk of your trip, and then ensure the risks do not outweigh the value of the purpose you're traveling for.

Taking the Lead

As you empower yourself with knowledge, tips, and techniques, you will naturally start to develop leadership skills, and all your training will surface as courage. That is what you want—to believe in yourself.

With all your preparation, you may very well find yourself being an example, and people around you will follow your lead. The reason? Most people are never trained, or even have a conversation, about making simple adjustments to keep themselves safe. Granted, people often do amazing things in times of crisis and horrible situations, but why rely solely on superhuman power or luck—that you may (or may not) have at that moment?

The initiative you're taking to learn and educate yourself could result in a scenario where everyone around you is panicking, and the fact that you are calm and running through your action options will immediately position you as a leader.

Don't be surprised when people look to you for guidance and decision making, or they just start to do what you are doing. The key here is you are in control and you know how to act; you aren't in the position to have to blindly follow someone else because you aren't prepared. You have acquired social awareness in a security sense that includes strategies for avoidance and action.

A crucial strategy is what's referred to as getting off the "X," (getting out of the target zone or line of fire), and it can mean the difference between survival or disaster. Speed and/or movement equal life if there is no cover or concealment. You will be deciding and acting as opposed to panicking and freezing.

Dangerous scenarios often fall into two categories: those that we get ourselves into, and those that are out of our control—perhaps we're just in the wrong place at the wrong time. Throughout the book, you've learned some really simple adjustments to your current mindless behavior—the actions or behaviors you don't think about at all—that will give you tools to avoid or defuse situations, increasing the likelihood of survival in either scenario.

Next, we'll explore some additional concepts to keep in mind as you continue to make adjustments to your daily activities and travel behavior.

Daily Adjustments

To increase your personal safety during day-to-day activities, here are some reminders about simple things you can start to think about as you go about your daily routine.

Walking

- Walk like you always know where you're going.
- Stand up straight.
- Make brief, confident eye contact with people around you.
  - * Authorities believe rapists and muggers target victims who appear vulnerable, weak, easily intimidated, or look to be daydreaming.
- Take note of who's behind you and if they're gaining on you. If you feel you're being followed, get to a well-lit area or duck into a business or someplace with lots of people.
- Lighten your load when walking; don't load yourself down with heavy or multiple bags.
- Know your route; when possible, avoid alleys, vacant lots, deserted streets, and construction sites.
- Don't allow anyone to put you in a car; fight if you can.

* If you do get put in a trunk:

- Kick out the taillights.
- Look/feel for the trunk release (required on all models after 2002).

Here's a fun little spy tip I learned: Use your cell phone as a mirror to look behind you (the blank screen is approximately 80% reflective). This is also a good tip to use in restaurants so you can see behind and around you. Act like you're checking your teeth or lipstick to casually check the area around and behind you.

Another tactic to use if you feel someone is following you is to reverse your camera and either snap a picture over your shoulder, off to the side, or stop to take a selfie, with the person behind you in the picture. What you're looking for is someone you recognize OR someone who is intentionally covering their face. That could be a sign they don't want you to see them. Red flags should immediately go up.

Parking and Parking Lots

You've been driving and parking in parking lots for years, right? It's not brain surgery. However, there are definitely things you can do and look for to keep yourself safe. Parking lots are a wonderful opportunity for predators to take advantage of single females walking alone, especially those who aren't paying attention to their surroundings (like looking at or talking on the phone). Start making an effort to do the following:

When arriving in a parking lot:

- Park near lighting/light poles, both during the day and at night. On occasion, you will inevitably enter a mall, business, or gym when it's daylight and exit after the sun has gone down. You don't want to be walking in the middle of a dark parking lot by yourself. It's much easier for someone to hide in the middle of a dark lot. You want to be near or under a light, which helps you see what's around the area. Light also offers exposure, and exposure is the last thing a predator wants. Park by the light, day or night, so that it becomes a habit to do so.

- When you leave your vehicle, walk in the middle of the aisle rather than between parked cars. It's easier for someone to reach out and grab you from between cars. If you're in the middle of the aisle, they have to risk more exposure to grab you or your purse. Those few extra steps for them means more time for you to react.

- Walk with purpose and confidence.

When leaving a parking lot:

- When you exit a building to return to your car, again, walk down the middle of the aisle.

- Have your keys out and hold one key between your fingers so you have the long, metal part of the key exposed.

- Note if someone is parked very close to your door, especially if there are open spots in the rest of the lot. If you have the option, go back to where you came from to ask someone to walk you to your car or watch you to your car. Or wait for someone else to be nearby before you approach your car and have your finger on the "panic" button of your car remote if you have one.

- If there is something under your windshield wiper or attached to your car in any way, DO NOT stop to remove it. This is often a tactic used to distract people so that someone has an opportunity to come up from behind, pull you away, or maybe shove you into a car. Share this information with your teenage drivers!

- Once you're in your car, don't sit there checking your phone, receipts, or anything else. Get your vehicle in motion and leave.

Parking Lots

As a kid, you were most likely taught not to walk down the middle of the aisle in a parking lot, right? You were always being told by your mom and dad to walk along the side, so you didn't get hit by a car. At the time, that was very good parenting and appropriate advice for a child. You were accompanied by an adult who was responsible for your safety.

However, as an adult female, you need to think about that a little differently, based on a different kind of risk. It now makes sense to walk in the middle of the aisle of a parking lot because it creates distance, providing a buffer between you and someone waiting to pull you into a vehicle or rob you. If there is a predator monitoring the lot for their next unsuspecting victim, and you're walking in the middle of the aisle, they'd have to show themselves and cover more ground to grab you. OR, if they see someone walking along the outside of the lane, meaning they can nab that person faster with less opportunity to be seen, who do you think they are going to choose?

At times, the things you were taught to do as a child need to be reevaluated. A small change in behavior can mean the difference between being a victim and being safe.

So, now, when you walk down the aisle of a parking lot, walk in the middle and move over when a car passes; then move back to the middle. I promise you won't get in trouble with your parents!

Teaching Your Kids

As you start to implement these small changes in your behavior, you'll inevitably be making an impression on your kids. But, be even more intentional—in addition to modeling these behaviors for your kids, find opportunities for teachable moments. Explain to them why you're doing what you're doing, like parking under a light when there might be closer spots or walking down the middle of the aisle.

Use these easy behavior changes to introduce good habits as they start to become more independent. I guarantee that YOU will feel better as your kids start driving and going places alone, because you know that you have given them a good foundation for everyday vigilance.

Chapter 4

Everyday Vigilance

Note: The highest rates of crime occur between 8:00 p.m. and 2:00 a.m. You can reduce your chances of becoming a victim by stopping for gas at 11:00 a.m. instead of 11:00 p.m.

Everyday vigilance is your ultimate goal. It means that you are aware of your surroundings and are generally alert to what's going on around you. You have a quiet confidence about you. You've become all-around savvy. You're shrewd and have practical knowledge, giving you the ability to make quick and good decisions. Knowing what to do in everyday situations gives you that extra edge.

Rest assured, the goal of all of this isn't to make you walk around in a complete state of paranoia. It's about building up your confidence, speeding up your thinking, and improving your response time. You want to raise your overall consciousness to serve yourself, your friends and family, your community, and ultimately your country.

Essentially, you're doing your part to be an extension of our national security by being personally responsible and taking the initiative to be vigilant. By having a trained eye and an understanding of when something should be reported, your power to have impact is immeasurable.

As we continue to drill down, it's important to understand and review how to apply these practices in everyday life.

Ingress/Egress: Get in the habit of noticing the entrances and exits of buildings, restaurants, theaters, hotels, airports, etc. Be familiar with where they are so that if something happens, where you need to go to get out safely is top of mind. Make it a habit to listen to all safety instructions when provided; we all have a tendency to tune them out.

Blending In: As much as we all like to stand out, knowing how to literally blend into a crowd can be one of the best defenses we have. People can be marked targets because they unintentionally draw attention to themselves. This happens in ways that we often don't think about, but once you know them, they are easy to modify or avoid altogether.

When you're traveling overseas or even in an area you are not familiar with, act, dress, and behave like those around you—much like the old saying, "When in Rome, do as the Romans do." Consider these points when traveling abroad:

- Leave the expensive, flashy jewelry at home.
- Don't bring branded luggage.
- Don't wear American sports team apparel.

- Backpacks are iconic symbols of Americans; leave them at home.

- Don't upgrade your rental car even if you have the option. Think about what class of car will be on the streets you're driving, and choose a car that will blend in.

- Walk at the pace of the crowd on the street. Don't walk too fast or slow.

- Carry a whistle; it's the most universal signal for help.

- Learn the word for help in the language of the country you'll be traveling to.

Avoiding Contact/Disengaging: Generally, women are kind and approachable. However, there are certainly situations where it's better not to engage in a conversation or completely avoid someone. And there are situations where you might just have to be a bitch. Don't feel bad or guilty about it. Yes, we should be kind and polite to one another, but when you're a female traveling by yourself, it's not necessary to make new friends. You will very likely never see these people again, so don't worry about coming across as rude; consider it a preemptive bump. Better safe than sorry.

Similarly, if you find yourself in a conversation or situation that you are growing uncomfortable with, don't be afraid to be direct and just abruptly end the conversation. And as much as I hate to have to bring it up, this also applies to business interactions. Unfortunately, some men (and a few women) don't understand boundaries. Or, they completely understand boundaries but choose to push them.

The beautiful thing about becoming vigilant and situationally aware is that you become much better at recognizing these behaviors early and stopping them before you find yourself in an uncomfortable place. You will also develop an air about you that exudes confidence. Most people see confidence as power and find it intimidating. That alone can make you an unattractive target. Perfect—mission accomplished!

Personal Tradecraft: Tradecraft is an old word that referred to the work, or craft, of any profession or trade. It probably acquired its specific link to spy work during World War II, though it is a word that is most heavily associated with the Cold War. It can also be related to techniques and procedures of information gathering that are useful in any context. Many law enforcement and military individuals will tend to sit or position themselves where they can scan a room.

Here are a couple more techniques you can add to your personal tradecraft toolbox:

- Always try to sit with your back to the wall so you can watch the doorways and what's going on in the area around you.
- Use windows as you walk by them and look to see if anyone is following you.
- Use the reflection of your cell phone as a mirror to see behind you or turn the camera around so you can discreetly snap a photo.

Establish a realistic awareness of possible threats: It is common to have an "I will be fine" mentality, which is exactly what a predator wants you to have because you have no guard up with that mindset. A significant facet of being vigilant is understanding when you could be vulnerable or in a dangerous area. Simply having a realistic mindset makes you more tuned in and likely to exhibit plugged-in body language and confidence.

A word of caution—you can be mentally plugged in, applying personal tradecraft, and essentially doing all the right things, but unconscious actions could be sacrificing all the good practices you're implementing. Be cognizant of the following, which could be telling signs that set you apart or mark you as easy prey:

- Don't take a cut rate taxi, even when they are the most convenient and available. Resist the urge in the moment to choose the quick and easy option.

- Don't drink too much; even moderate alcohol intake can lower awareness.

- Never leave your drink unattended or accept a drink from a stranger; this is a great opportunity for someone to put a "roofie" in it, otherwise known as the date rape drug. Watch your drink being poured if you can.

- Don't fish around in your purse for money, lipstick, etc. when you're in public.

- Don't fumble with maps.

- Don't be obvious about being in an unfamiliar area.

- Walk down the middle of the sidewalk.

- Stand back from the curb while waiting to cross the street.

If you do experience an uneasy feeling, engage your principles of vigilance:

- Look around.

- Walk with your shoulders back and your head up.

- If you have a personal safety app on your phone, have it at the ready, or you can put 911 in and be ready to hit "Send" if you need to.

- If necessary, alter your path and quickly get to a public place with people and lights.

- Don't panic. Remain calm so that you can think clearly and process your options for opportunities to get to a safe place.

Mindful Vigilance

As a longtime yoga instructor, the connection between mindfulness and vigilance is very clear to me, though at first glance, most people don't see the relationship. When you practice mindfulness, you are always taking in your surroundings, noticing smells, sounds, and beauty. You are fully present. That presence, when applied to your personal awareness, will automatically increase your personal vigilance.

Mindfulness also provides recovery and rest for your brain. Just like you take a rest day after an intense workout—so your muscles recover and heal—mindfulness helps give your brain the break it needs to become stronger. This practice creates space for you to think and be in the moment.

Mindfulness and meditation are similar in that both are hygiene for your brain. But, they are not the same thing. For our discussion, here is how we will define them:

- Mindfulness is bringing your full mind or attention to a place or object.

- Meditation is when you intentionally set time aside to practice achieving a mentally clear and emotionally calm state.

Today, we live in a mode of constant, but partial, attention. There have been studies showing that we check email 75 times a day, social media 20 times, and that we are interrupted every 3 minutes. With those stats, there's no question as to why we aren't present at any given moment—the brain can't switch gears effectively that fast and that often.

As a result, we suffer from mental chatter and "monkey mind." Monkey mind is when your thoughts resemble a monkey swinging from tree to tree. You're jumping from one thought to another so quickly that you end up with a mind filled with partial thoughts, to-do's, open-ended questions, worries, and so on.

All of that results in mental clutter that occupies so much of your mental processing that it takes you out of the present moment. You know the types of thoughts that can take over: Perhaps you're replaying conversations in your head, kicking yourself because now you have the best comeback, but couldn't come up with it in the moment (we've all been there); Or, you're focused on your to-do list, continuously reciting it in your head so you don't forget it.

All of this mental chatter keeps you from being present. It means you're completely preoccupied so you're not paying attention to what's going on around you. When you clear mental clutter, you create space for the things that can serve you and help you live in the present. You can notice your surroundings for beauty (mindfulness) and safety (vigilance).

Mindfulness and meditation connect in many ways. There are numerous health benefits you can attribute to the practice of mindfulness and meditation, but for the purpose of this discussion, I'm going to focus on those connected to our topic of self-protection.

Practicing meditation and mindfulness improves both your health (the state of complete physical, mental and social well-being and not merely the absence of disease) and wellness (the process of making choices toward a healthy and more fulfilling life). I've seen these outcomes described as follows:

Wellness (including mental and physical) = Happiness
Health (including mental and physical) = Freedom

When you're happy, you have energy and motivation that lead you to make good decisions. Those decisions can result in better health, and a healthy person is better able to take care of themselves. Not having risk factors, such as heart disease and high blood pressure, will be an advantage in a threatening situation. In addition, healthy habits of mindfulness will reduce anxiety and improve focus, self-control, and sleep—all things that play a part in your personal safety and strengthen your confidence.

If you don't feel you currently possess healthy habits, there are tools you can use to help you develop them. Below is a very simple form of meditation that you can try.

Meditation and Concentration

Meditation and concentration are complementary. Only true concentration will lead to meditation. If you have a steady mind, you will see all other aspects of your life as steady and balanced.

To achieve this, you can try concentrating on internal aspects—focus on your breathing, or count numbers or your heartbeat in your mind. Alternatively, you can concentrate on external aspects—the flame of a candle, a point on the wall, or the ticking of a clock.

Learning to concentrate successfully will require some practice at first. Don't give up when you feel your mind wandering. Acknowledge the thought, then push it out and begin the process again.

Practicing Concentration Meditation

The goal of building your concentration is to eliminate all distractions, whether external or internal. Being able to concentrate during meditation will prove its benefits in your everyday life. There are three simple steps in this process:

Focus on Your Breathing

Find a comfortable spot and allow your mind to be cleared of all thoughts. Now, just focus on your breathing as you inhale and exhale. You can count your breaths.

Try to Not Move

It is common to be uncomfortable or fidgety at first, since you may not yet be used to sitting still for a long period of time. Close your eyes, find a comfortable position, and just calm your mind. You will notice your body loosening up and becoming still as well.

Use a Mantra

Once you are comfortable, choose a mantra. This can be any syllable, word, or phrase which will help you focus. The most popular choice of word for meditation is "Om."

Mindfulness and Breathing

Breathing techniques offer a great introduction to begin a mindfulness practice. This is a perfect time to focus inward, using your breath to inhale what you need and exhale what is no longer serving you.

A basic breathing technique is called Equal Part Breathing, where you inhale and exhale for equal counts. For example: inhale for three counts and exhale for three counts. On the inhale think about what it is you need (strength, confidence, peace, courage, etc.) and visualize filling your body with that. On the exhale, consciously expel anything that isn't serving you anymore (a bad conversation, anxiety, fear, worry). This is a powerful and empowering practice, one that can also serve you well in multiple areas of your life. Breathing calms the nervous system. Knowing how to properly breathe in a dangerous or tense situation can help give you the calm and control you need to think yourself to a safe place.

You can also take this practice and apply guided imagery, where you visualize yourself in dangerous scenarios and see yourself getting out safely. Guided imagery (sometimes called guided meditation, visualization, mental rehearsal, or guided self-hypnosis) is a gentle but powerful technique that focuses the imagination in proactive, positive ways. This practice is used in professional sports, military training, and even medical treatment.

Visualize yourself in a calm state, thinking and making your way out of a hypothetical situation. While you're doing that, maybe apply a self-defense move you're comfortable with (eye jab, palm to the nose, knee to the groin, punch to the throat) and see yourself doing that in your mind's eye. Make sure you finish the thought and don't forget to mentally rehearse seeing yourself running in the other direction once that move has been made. Remember, in a crisis situation, you will revert to what you were trained to do, so make sure you train your brain to run away.

With practice, habits will begin to form and being mindful will become your norm. Your mindful state will naturally make you vigilant. When you apply all the small adjustments—holding your head up and shoulders back, walking with purpose, making brief eye contact, scanning your surroundings, and noticing, you will have an air about you. This air will come across as a quiet confidence.

A quiet confidence not only serves you well on the street but will come into play in other areas of your life. Compare the small adjustments that you make to the butterfly effect, the theory whereby a tiny, isolated change in a complex system can have large effects elsewhere. I'm going use the definition loosely here. In today's society, our personal boundaries need to be crystal clear and fortified, because people, both male and female, are constantly testing them. Our boundaries are tested at work, in social settings, and with family.

The way you carry and present yourself can put out a nonverbal vibe that you are not someone who will tolerate your boundaries being crossed. In a work setting, this may prevent an unwanted advance. In social settings, it may bump the creep that has ill intentions (like striking up a conversation with you and then waiting for the opportunity to put something in your drink). Within your family, you won't be the one constantly approached for money or favors, because relatives know your boundaries can't be breached.

The butterfly effect applies to all of the things that we've talked about so far, in that the small adjustments that you make now (and model for others), can have a huge impact in the future. You won't be the someone whose boundaries others will cross. And while this isn't a book about the #MeToo movement, having a quiet confidence and strong boundaries are two great examples of how something that you instill now has the potential to ward off inappropriate behavior in the future.

Additional Breathing Exercise

Controlled Breath (Tactical Breathing)

- Inhale for four counts
- Stop and hold the breath for four counts.
- Exhale for four counts.
- Repeat.

This simple technique helps control your breath and can counteract the shallow breathing and shaking effects that occur when too much adrenaline is in your system.

Chapter 5

Travel Safety

Janet, now in her early 60s, shared with me that when she was "young and dumb," she used to hitchhike. She said that one time, which was also her last hitchhike ride, as soon as she got into the car, she had a bad feeling. The hair on her arms stood straight up, her heart rate increased, her palms became clammy, and she immediately regretted getting in the car.

However, she remained calm. She didn't want to let the driver sense she was nervous. So, she did some very quick thinking and pulled a bit of guerilla reverse psychology out of her back pocket. She said, "I am so glad it was you who picked me up. There are a lot of sketchy people out there, but I can tell you're not one of them."

Needless to say, she made it safely to her next stop, but if that driver did have ill intentions, she might have set an expectation for him that he felt he had to live up to.

Because you are now very aware and cognizant of your surroundings, you are going to pick up on cues and things that feel "off" around you. You now know to trust your gut, because you understand your natural instincts to avoid danger.

Before we dive into understanding a predator, here are a few of their personality traits:

- No conscience
- Cold
- Remorseless
- Indifferent to damage they cause
- Have an evil streak
- Emotionless
- Use words as tool to manipulate and coerce

Note that predators can come across as "nice," but niceness and goodness aren't the same thing. Goodness requires honorable intentions. John Wayne Gacy, Jr., the serial killer and sexual predator, would dress up and perform as a clown for neighborhood kids. While investigators were exhuming 26 corpses from his Illinois home, his neighbor was busy explaining what a nice guy he was.

Make sure you know someone's intentions before you let down your guard. This is even more essential when traveling and outside your familiar places and routines. When you're traveling, you need to remain particularly alert and vigilant.

Why Would I Be a Target?

In many developing countries, kidnapping and ransom are one of the top five industries. Additionally, outside of the United States, there is a common misconception that all Americans are rich.

Therefore, Americans often are seen as ideal targets because they could fetch a handsome ransom that their American family, or even better their company, could and would pay. Criminals and terrorist organizations often target executives and employees of large corporations because these individuals are associated with wealth or perceived media value.

Since criminals prefer targets who don't intimidate them, women are thought of as an easier take. What follows are some specific tips to keep in mind when you're traveling to avoid being targeted; a few of these suggestions may go against some of your natural inclinations.

Travel Attire

Companies look for every opportunity to make a consumer impression, imprinting their name on anything and everything—from pens to golf bags. When you're with a company for a long time, it seems like your entire closet consists of logo-emblazoned apparel and tchotchke items.

However, when you're traveling, leave those items in the closet. All of those jackets, shirts, hats, etc., send a message to predators that you work for a company that would pay a good ransom to get their valuable employee back. When traveling, be benign. Don't wear anything that makes you stand out in a crowd or advertises who you work for.

Telltale Signs

Bad guys will be on the lookout for anything that identifies you as an American.

- Keep luggage clear of any company identity.
- Don't put a visible business card in your luggage tag.
- Wear understated clothing with no USA and/or American flags visible.
- Don't advertise that you are with a large company.
- Don't wear American sports team apparel.

Rental Cars

As a frequent business traveler, it's a natural reaction to accept a car upgrade, especially when it's at no additional cost. However, something as simple as that could put you on someone's radar. When you do your travel prep, research the culture and environment at your destinations.

Be conscious of what you need to do to blend in, starting when you drive off of the rental car lot. If you are offered an upgrade to a luxury car, but the majority of cars on the streets will be 1980–90s models, you are going to stand out. You don't want to give anyone a reason to notice you in a crowd, whether it be while walking down the sidewalk or driving on the street.

Counter Surveillance

I will keep reiterating that when you start getting that uneasy feeling in your gut, you need to act on it. If you're walking through an airport, a hotel, or a public place, and you get a sense that you someone is following you, here are a few techniques you can use to confirm:

- If you're walking in a crowd or on the street and you sense someone is gaining ground on you, stop abruptly and turn around. Quickly scan for someone who covers their face, looks away, or maybe goes to light a cigarette; you're looking for someone who is intentionally trying not to be seen. They might be fearful that you would recognize them from somewhere else, or they don't want you to be able to identify them later.

- If you are on an escalator and you have a sense that someone is following you, ride the escalator to the top of the platform and then quickly get back on and ride it down. As you do that, look over at those riding up. Again, scan for anyone who is intentionally looking the other direction or covering their face.

- Refer back to some of the techniques that were discussed earlier, like using your phone to see behind you, turning your camera around to snap a picture behind you, and using glass windows and doors to see who's behind you.

Body Language

How a person uses their space is a big indicator of intent. Be wary if someone encroaches on your personal space, which is typically 18-inches to five feet, or if they move into what's deemed the intimate zone of contact, which ranges from zero to 18-inches. If you haven't invited someone to move closer, it shows, at best, a lack of awareness. It can also show a lack of respect for your boundaries or, at worst, an intention to trap or harm you.

You need to be vigilant about your space. You decide who comes into it, and how close they are allowed to be. Predators look for opportunities to have you within arm's length where they can attack, subdue, or drug you. Protecting your space is critical.

Tells

If you find yourself in a standoff or other generally uncomfortable situation, watch for the bad guy to stretch and yawn. This is a semi-involuntary reaction the body has when stressed and/or getting ready to act. They are stretching the muscles and yawning to increase oxygen in the blood. They may not even know they are doing it.

Pay attention to yourself next time you're in a stressful situation; see if you notice yourself doing the same thing. Inexperienced bad guys will tend to do it more. Law enforcement officers will look for this sign to recognize if someone is getting ready to run or fight.

Another subconscious telltale sign is the direction someone's feet are pointing when talking to you. People have a tendency to face their feet in the direction they're getting ready to go. Police officers also shared that people will give off other micro signs of their intentions, like glancing in the direction they are looking to go. If someone stops you to ask a question and turns their upper body toward you but keeps their feet facing in the other direction, that's another subconscious sign that they may intend to trap or grab you (or your bag).

Be cautious of someone with only one hand in their pocket. Unless specifically reaching for something, people tend to keep both hands in or out of their pockets. Try it. It's unnatural to have only one hand in a pocket.

As you read through this book, keep in mind there isn't one specific way or situation where you can apply this information. Use this new knowledge to stay safe, Keep your thought process fluid. Think nimbly. Recognize that in most situations you have options, and your ability to trust yourself to act can mean the difference between being a victim or victor. Continuously innovate the way you keep yourself safe.

BTK Killer's Tips on How to Not Be Killed

"You know, lately I've been thinking about what people can do to protect themselves from guys like me, and I came up with a little list," he said. "I guess most of it is pretty obvious, but I'll tell it to you if you like."

"I'm all ears," I said.

"The first thing I'd suggest for a woman living alone is to get a security system," he said. "For women living alone, I think the most important thing they can do is give the impression that they live with a man. Maybe have some men's clothes scattered around the house or leave a toiletry kit out in the open, just in case someone breaks in to scope the place out.

It would also be wise to have two dogs-one outside and another one inside. And on the answering machine, have a man's voice on the outgoing recording. And you know how I used to cut the phone lines of houses? People should always check their phones whenever they enter their houses. Maybe since everyone has cell phones these days, maybe that's not so important.... But I do think it's a good idea to always leave the radio on in your house and avoid routines. Never take the same route to and from work or someplace like the grocery store.

And the last thing would be for women to be extra suspicious of vehicles they see parked out in front of their house or apartment. I often used to drive back to my victim's homes over and over again and park out in front."

Excerpt from "Inside the Mind Of BTK" (pages 314-315), by John Douglas and Johnny Dodd.

Chapter 6

Travel Prep

Perhaps you've been traveling for years and are a pro at getting your clothes, toiletries, and work materials packed efficiently. However, to become a vigilant traveler, there are a few more things you need to incorporate into your travel prep routine to ensure your safety.

While many of these tips have traditionally been applied primarily to international travel, that has changed. Over the past few years, there have been unexpected flare-ups of violence domestically. Safety experts now recommend travelers prepare for all situations, whether traveling domestically or internationally.

Before You Go

What follows are tips on how to research, prepare, and organize for a trip. If you aren't already doing these tasks, think about adding them into your travel prep routine:

- Make copies of your passport and leave one copy at home. It's a good idea to take a picture of your passport with your phone.

- Make copies of your insurance card. It is also a good idea to keep a picture of insurance information on your phone.

- When traveling abroad, do your research on what's going on in the region. Identify any risks or threats for the region to which you're traveling. An excellent pre-travel resource is provided by the US Department of State at Travel.State.Gov.

- Prepare a reference sheet that has phone numbers and websites in case your phone is lost, stolen, or destroyed. We depend on our phones (especially when traveling) and typically store everything from tickets to hotel reservations on them. This is very convenient until something happens, and we are without our phone. Then, we are absolutely helpless. I challenge you to recite from memory your boss's phone number. If you can, kudos to you! Most can't. Creating a paper reference sheet can be very useful if you lose your phone and need to reach an airline, rental car company, hotel, etc. In this situation, you can't easily look these numbers up, and it's unlikely you're going to find a phone booth or phonebook as a resource.

- If you're traveling abroad and being assigned security or an executive car service, make sure you are 100 percent comfortable with both services. To do this, get as much information as possible by asking specific questions, including company name, security detail or driver's name, type of car, pick-up and drop-off locations, contact information for security and driver, specific details on how to contact security and driver, etc. You should be aware that cartels or underground networks often control these types of service businesses. In that case, you have a "company" that makes their living off kidnapping and ransom (among many other illegal activities). So, they now know who you are, what company you work for, where you are going to be, when you're going to be there, etc.

- Make sure when travelling internationally that you have the address and phone number of the American embassy or consulate.

Airports

- Schedule direct flights, whenever possible. Avoid stops at airports or areas deemed high risk by the US Department of State. Detailed information on countries with travel advisories can be found at Travel.State.Gov.

- Minimize time in airport public areas by moving quickly from check-in to security screening to the airport's secured gate areas. Once you arrive at your destination, leave the airport as soon as you have your belongings. Arrival areas tend to be less secure than departure areas.

- While in the airport, notice if something is out of place. Specifically, keep watch for abandoned briefcases, packages, or other suspicious items. If you do notice something amiss, report it to the nearest airport authority and leave the area.

- Play it cool and try to avoid bringing extra attention to yourself.

- If for some reason your flight is delayed or canceled, and you're forced to spend the night at the airport, use your belt to attach your belongings to you. Weave the belt through your briefcase handle, purse, and any other bags you have. Make sure you place the buckle near your body, so you are more likely to feel any tampering.

Airplanes

- When getting on a plane, count the seats to the closest exit row or door. This will come in handy if the plane is dark or filled with smoke, and you need to find your way out. Those within five rows of an exit have the highest chance of survival in the event of a crash.

- Having a basic knowledge of customs and rituals could help you recognize if someone is behaving suspiciously prior to boarding. For example, some suicide bombers have a ritual they do prior to sacrificing themselves.

- Do not share personal information or details about your business trip with seatmates. They may have no ill intentions; however, people around you can overhear your conversation and take note.

Remembering these few tips may make all the difference between being safe and having to deal with a dangerous situation.

Chapter 7

Transitions

If you've ever taken a yoga class, you've probably heard the instructor talk about transitions. Moving or transitioning from one position into another is as important as the final pose itself. However, it's natural to mindlessly move from one pose to another and not check in until you're fully into the pose.

Oftentimes, we treat traveling from place to place much like transitions in yoga practice. We move from one place to another without really paying much attention to what's going on as we travel. But, it is during this timeframe that we can be the most vulnerable, especially when not paying attention.

There are a few simple things you can do to reduce your vulnerability when traveling from place to place. It starts by paying attention to your surroundings rather than just being a checked-out passenger. Here are a few tips for those transitional times when traveling. At these moments, a little extra attention and awareness can help keep you safe.

Transportation

Rental Car

- If you get bumped from behind, do not stop; drive to a populated area. You can also call 911 to have authorities meet you somewhere.

- If you get to your car and there is something on the windshield or under the wiper, leave it in place (assuming you can see enough to drive) and get to a populated area before you remove it. This is a tactic used by predators to keep you outside of your car so that someone can approach you.

- In the event of a breakdown or other emergency, know your rental car company's phone number.

- When stopped for a train, leave at least one car length between you and the car in front of you. This gives you enough space to maneuver if you begin to feel uncomfortable about your surroundings. It also prevents someone from intentionally blocking you in.

- Keep your windows rolled up and doors locked at all times.

Taxi

- Be cautious when paying with a credit card in a taxi. Many have been known to have skimming devices on the credit card reader.

- The position of power in a taxi is sitting behind the driver. Sitting behind the driver provides you the option to take action if you are threatened. You would have the option of choking, gouging eyes, or using an improvised weapon of some sort if you had to.

- Use a map app on your phone to follow the route being taken to your destination. Even if you're unfamiliar with the area you're traveling in, you'll know if you are going in a completely opposite direction and can say something. You want to let the driver know you are paying attention.

Uber/Lyft

- Get familiar with the app and review the safety features so you know how to use them. They continue to add new ones.

- Request your ride while still inside to avoid standing outside alone.

- Check the license plate (and even snap a picture before you get in), confirm that the driver's photo and name match what's listed in the app. Uber/Lyft rides can only be requested through the app. Do not get in a car at any location with a driver you have not requested via the app or with one who claims to be with Uber /Lyft and offers an unrequested ride.

- Prior to getting into an Uber/Lyft, ask the driver the name of the person they are picking up; don't tell them your name first.

- Ride in the back seat, it allows you to exit on either side of the street and gives you and your driver personal space.

- Share your route on the app with your boss, colleagues, family, or someone else you trust so they know when you've arrived safely. If you didn't know that was an option on the Uber/Lyft app, now you do!

- Follow your intuition and trust your instincts when riding in an Uber/Lyft. If something doesn't feel right, call 911 immediately.

Public Transportation

- Don't sit by the door/exit on a bus/train; it's easier to be robbed or attacked by a criminal on foot.

- Note who gets on and off the bus/train with you. Keep your head up, looking around, and make eye contact to send a message to anyone who may be sizing you up. Those small proactive measures can send a strong message of "Don't even try it."

Car Service

Car services can provide a higher sense of security, and in most cases, your sense would be correct. However, know that in some countries, transportation companies and other businesses are controlled by organized crime groups.

Here's a scenario that will help you think like the enemy:

You arrange for a car service to pick you from the airport. The driver/car service company now knows:

- What company you are with
- Where you are staying
- That you are traveling alone
- Where you're going to be and when; especially if they are transporting you while you're there on business
- When you are leaving

That makes you an easy, coordinated hit. I don't share that with you to scare you, but so you can confirm that your car service has been vetted by your employer. Remember, kidnapping and ransom is a legitimate industry in many foreign countries. While the risk is slight, it's still good to understand and be aware that it is a risk.

Hotels

Hotels become our home away from home, but that doesn't necessarily mean you would want all the guests in the lobby to sit in your living room. Just like you would assess anyone coming into your home, you need to make sure you're aware of who's coming and going in the public areas of the hotel (lobby, restaurant, bar) as well as what the surrounding neighborhood is like.

Checking In

As soon as you enter the lobby, eyes go up. Scan the area and take note of anything that looks suspicious or sets off any bells. Enact all of your strong body language techniques and leave the "nice lady" disposition at the entrance. I'm not suggesting you should lose all common courtesy and be downright rude; however, there is a difference between being polite and being gullible. Hotel lobbies are an ideal place for predators to blend in and size guests up as they walk into (and out of) hotels.

When checking in:

- Use valet parking whenever possible.
- Wear a "wedding ring" and sign in as "Mrs."
- Note who is standing beside you when you're giving your name.
- Keep your belongings between you and check-in desk
- Request a room that is on floor 3–7. Floors 1 and 2 have a higher chance of quick-hit petty crimes due to easier entry and exit. And in the event of a fire, fire truck ladders cannot reach above the 7th floor.
- Make sure when the desk assistant gives you your key, they don't announce your room number out loud. For example, "Mrs. Smith, you will be on the 4th floor in room 425." If that happens, kindly ask that they reassign you and just write the room number down for you.
- As you leave the check-in desk, scan the area again and just make mental notes.

As you head to your room, there are even elevator tips to keep you safe:

- Position yourself next to the elevator's control panel. You want to be next to the alarm button and start/stop button.

- If you enter the elevator first, ask anyone who enters with you their floor first. If you get a bad gut feeling about a fellow elevator rider, regardless of your floor number, push a floor number above theirs so you force them off. You don't want to push a floor below just to get off earlier because they could follow you off.

- In a crowded elevator, maneuver your way to the control panel as people get off.

- Don't feel like you have to make small talk with people on the elevator. You'll likely never see this person again, so better safe than sorry.

- Don't look at your phone or disengage mentally; keep your head up.

In the Room

- Look for fire exits/stairways in the halls and note the closest one to your room.

- Keep your room neat so you'll notice disturbed or missing items quickly.

- If there is civil unrest during your trip, stay in the room.

- Don't open the door or accept packages delivered to the room until you verify with the front desk. Room service is an expected delivery.

- Do not discuss your business or travel plans in public areas where they can be overheard.

- Take a rubber door stopper. There are also portable door locks you can purchase.

- Get in the habit of keeping your room key on the nightstand (next to the bed) so you always know where it is in case you have to make a quick room exit.

Chapter 8

Improvised Weapons

As we've been discussing throughout this book, your personal protection needs to be an ongoing innovative process. It's important to continually evaluate and adapt safety habits to add more layers of prevention and protection.

An essential part of this process means exploring and understanding new ways to be cautious while holding your ground in a way that deters predators. Ideally, we've prepared so well to prevent and protect that we only rarely have to act.

If you do happen to find yourself in a scary situation, don't automatically put yourself in an underdog position. Your mind, confidence, and force are all very powerful weapons and often your best resource. However, various everyday items can provide help if you get creative with how you use them.

Personal Protection

A simple change to improve your personal protection involves carrying a flashlight in your purse. When traveling, a flashlight can be used to help find your way out of a burning hotel or provide additional light when walking to your car. In a self-defense role, it can be used to blind someone when shined directly in their eyes or used as a weapon to hit an attacker in a soft spot: temple, eye, mouth, throat, groin.

When you change your mindset and think innovatively, everyday items that are either on your person or present all around you can become very effective self-defense tools. We're going to refer to these items as improvised weapons. While that may sound intimidating, it simply means you're using a common object in a different manner or for a different purpose than it's normally used.

An effective improvised weapon has a few, useful characteristics. Specifically, these objects have one or more of the following features: solid and has density; capable of causing damage; and/or extends your reach.

Things that have a solid density include:

- Cell phones – palm the phone and hit an attacker's nose with the flat part of the screen
- Purses – use your entire purse as a club
- Lipstick – use as a jabbing device for soft spots

Things that can cause damage include:

- Pens/Pencils
- Nail files
- High heels

- Hand sanitizer – squirt it in eyes
- Bobby pins
- Keys

Things that can extend your reach:

- Umbrella – use as a club or shield
- Cane – club, poke, or hook a leg
- Hairspray/perfume – spray in eyes

The element of surprise and a couple of quick forceful punches can be very effective. Be sure that you've prepared by using your visualization techniques. You need to visualize yourself doing that action. Better yet, practice on a bag or padded-up person when possible. Make sure you also condition your mind to run in the opposite direction after you've acted. As silly as it sounds, it's not an uncommon reaction to freeze in place; you have to see yourself deliver the blow and run away.

Next time you're on a plane, sitting at your desk, or perhaps in a public place, pause for a moment and look around to identify anything and everything that you could use in an emergency situation. Make this a bit of a game. What you're doing is practicing your innovative mindset and exercising your OODA loop, where you're able to quickly observe, orient, decide, and act.

Look around and see how many things you have within arm's reach to use as a weapon. Get creative and try to think of how you could use an object to buy a few seconds of time to distract or escape. Play this game with your older kids. Get them to learn to think on their feet. The result? You quickly realize you are not helpless. You have options and don't have to be a victim.

SOS Phone Features

Personal safety has also benefited from technological innovations. Many of these advances use phones to share information and alert people when help is needed. Google Play and the App Store offer a number of personal safety apps. Consider downloading one to give you an additional layer of personal safety. Search SOS in either app store.

Additionally, many iPhone and Android phones come with a built-in SOS feature. Google your phone to find out how to activate this capability. Keep in mind, you're going to have to practice using this feature just as you have to practice all of your other personal protection techniques.

In a highly stressful moment, your fine motor skills are possibly going to be gone. You're going to have to recall how to activate the SOS signal and then get your shaking fingers to work. This is an exercise you should practice when you have one of those adrenaline-pumping life moments but are not in danger. Regardless of how you train your brain, knowing how to activate the SOS feature needs to be second nature. Like many of the things we've been talking about throughout the book, take a moment to demonstrate this feature for your kids, too.

Chapter 9

Cybersafety

Data Theft, Viruses, and Malware

Computers, tablets, and smartphones contain a great deal of important information, ranging from corporate data and intellectual property to your own personal information. When traveling, it's especially important to protect your information. There are some basic things you can do to guard against theft and limit exposure to viruses and malware.

Keep these things in mind:

- Avoid connecting your device to public Wi-Fi networks if at all possible. That includes hotel Wi-Fi networks, which tend to be breeding grounds for viruses and malware. If you must use public networks, only log in to a secure Wi-Fi system. A password on the connection does not guarantee security, but it helps. If in doubt, ask. You want to hear WPA somewhere in the response.

- To avoid Wi-Fi networks, use your mobile phone as a mobile hotspot, then connect your computer to your phone. The cell network provides additional security since it is encrypted from the service provider to you. It's worth spending the extra money for the extra protection.

- Encrypt your laptop. By turning on or installing encryption software, you'll encrypt your hard drive. On a Mac, turn on FileVault. For Windows, turn on BitLocker (it comes with Windows 10 Professional). If you have an older version of Windows, you can purchase the software.

- When traveling internationally, use a dedicated laptop. Your IT department may already require and supply it, but if not, you can do it on your own.

  * Dedicate an old computer and load all of your necessary programs on it.

  * Then, make an image disc to replicate the entire operating system, programs, and settings. A free, easy-to-use imaging system is Clonezilla.

  * Take all the files you need on an encrypted jump drive. Once you've purchased an encryption system (e.g., BitLocker), you should use it on all of your USB drives as well. You don't even have to use different passwords (but that would be helpful).

  * When you return, erase everything from your drive and reinstall from your image disc.

  * If you bring back new or modified files, store them on your encrypted USB drive. Turn the drive over to your Information Security department for malware analysis and cleansing.

By following this process, you limit the potential of exposing your company's information and wipe out any viruses that you may have picked up while traveling. You don't want to risk spreading a virus throughout your organization when you reconnect to your company or personal network.

When traveling, there are other creative hacking risks out there. Be aware that leaving your computer unattended in a hotel room is extremely risky, especially if you're traveling in areas known for intellectual property piracy.

There are countries where state-sponsored data harvesting is required of hotel staff. They are provided with USB drives that they insert into your laptop while you're away and download all of your data while they are cleaning the room. (It's called DirtyMaid if you want to look it up.)

Another common way to access private data can occur when someone gets between you and the router. In this position, they can intercept your personal and company information. Protect yourself by practicing prevention:

- Cover your laptop's camera and microphone.
- If you see someone with an Alfa Modem (see below), take notice. This device can be used in "promiscuous mode," which allows the user to communicate with the router (that you're likely connected to unless you're using your hotspot) on another level. They can potentially download your entire hard drive without you even knowing it.

Here's what a typical Alfa router looks like.

Phishing

Phishing is when scammers use electronic communication to pose as trustworthy entities. From this place of trust, they make a fraudulent attempt to obtain sensitive information—like passwords, credit card details, bank account numbers, etc.

For example, if someone has compromised your email by cloning a familiar name in your address book and asks for personal data, you need to recognize the bait. Always check the email address. You will often notice that the domain from which it's sent is bogus and/or doesn't match the company/person it appears to come from.

To confirm whether you're being phished, you want to reply via an alternate method. This is called replying out-of-band. That means changing the mode of communication. If someone contacts you via email, you respond via phone or text. If someone texts, you respond via email.

How Would You Handle This?

You receive an email from someone in your firm's accounting department requesting your business credit card number. They are the ones who issue it, so you know immediately that you should be cautious.

Scammers can clone email headers to make themselves appear to be someone you know and who might be in your address book. If the email seems suspicious, trust your instinct and reply back by either calling or texting the person. If you respond back via email, you could likely be communicating directly with the scammer who is trying to steal your information.

Remember, they have cloned that address. So replying-out-of-band means responding via an alternate method to prove or disprove whether the email is legitimate:

- If emailed: reply via text or phone
- If texted: reply via email or phone
- If called: reply via email or text

Website Check

Websites can also be full of hidden cyber-dangers. Here are a few tools that you can quickly reference to verify (before entering any personal information) if a website is legitimate:

- **VirusTotal.com**—checks website URLs and files for viruses or malware (free service provided by Google)

- **WhoIs.com**—allows you to search and discover who owns domain names

- **CentralOps.net**—provides access to a collection of free online network utility tools

Passwords

Password protection is particularly important and can be hard for users to manage. Passwords have become more difficult to protect due to advances in automated online dictionaries that hackers use to access your data.

However, rest assured, there are methods of password protection that can help manage and protect passwords. These systems utilize random password generation, token keys, and dongles. If you'd like to try out one of these automated password methods, I suggest you search "Top 3 password protection tools" and see what's the latest and greatest. Another suggested search would be for "Two-factor authentication token devices" on Amazon. Yubikey and RSA are two reliable options. Yubikey is an easy hardware solution that is so reliable many companies use it for employee authentication, but it's just as effective for at-home use.

Physical Security

It may sound obvious, but don't leave your mobile device out where someone can grab it. If you're not currently using it, store it in a bag, briefcase, backpack, etc. While this won't stop determined thieves, it makes it harder to take, and it will be less obvious what you're carrying. Be particularly careful in airports and as you go through security screening. Amazingly, 1,200 laptops are left in airports every week!

If someone tries to take your mobile device or laptop by force, LET THEM HAVE IT! Don't fight them for it and possibly be physically injured, or worse. Remember that if you've encrypted the device, there is no way to get to the content. A laptop or phone can be replaced. You can't be.

Electronic Payments

Whenever possible, use mobile payment systems rather than your credit or debit card, especially when traveling. ApplePay, AndroidPay, and SamsungPay offer electronic payment systems tied to your mobile device. Your (credit or debit) card number is not stored on your device. Even if you are separated from your device, you can still use your payment cards for emergencies because the number has not been compromised.

Chapter 10

Active Shooter

Who would ever have thought we would need to talk about what to do during an active shooter situation, especially while traveling on an average business trip? Unfortunately, today's environment requires us to have this conversation. It's especially important because not only will it be scary and chaotic, but if it happens while you're traveling, you're more likely to be in an unfamiliar place and will need to revert to your training to stay calm. In the end, you'll be responsible for your own safety.

Profile of an Active Shooter

US government agencies define an active shooter as "an individual who is actively engaged in killing or attempting to kill people in a confined and populated area. In most cases, active shooters use firearms and there is no pattern or method to their selection of victims."[9]

---

[9] "Active Shooter - Definition." *ALICE Training Institute*, www.alicetraining.com/active-shooter/.

Active shooter situations occur with unexpected speed, and the events that follow are unpredictable. While it's very likely that law enforcement will be called as soon as the shooting starts, it takes an average of seven minutes before help will arrive on the scene. In these situations, those seven minutes will feel like seven years, and you will need to keep yourself safe until law enforcement arrives.

Additionally, active shooter situations start and end quickly—often within 10-15 minutes. They end quickly because either the shooter takes their own life or is shot by law enforcement. A less likely possibility is that shooter takes a hostage(s).

Mental and Physical Preparation

Active shooter situations require mental and physical preparation. You need to have a plan of action to keep yourself safe until the danger has passed. This means having the right mindset—being prepared to do whatever it takes to survive.

Fortunately, there are things you can do. The most well-known courses of action are Run/Evacuate, Hide, Take Action, and Fight. The following list details specific actions to take during an active shooter situation.[10]

Run/Evacuate

Determine whether there is an accessible escape route and try to evacuate the premises. Keep in mind the following tips:

---

[10] Eastwood, Joey. "Active Shooter at Work: How to Respond." *Stratus.hr*, 23 Oct. 2017, stratus.hr/2017/10/19/active-shooter-workplace/.

- Have an escape route and plan in mind.
- Evacuate whether others agree to go or not.
- Leave behind all of your belongings.
- Help others get away, if possible.
- Prevent others from entering spaces where an active shooter could be.
- Keep your hands visible.
- Listen and follow instructions given by any police officers.
- Do not try to move injured or wounded people.
- Call 911 when you are in a safe location.

Hide

If unable to evacuate the area, find someplace to hide where the active shooter is less likely to find you. You should look for a hiding place where you can:

- Be out of the active shooter's view.
- Find protection if shots are fired in your direction.
- Maintain movement options. Don't get trapped or limit escape options.

To prevent an active shooter from entering your hiding place:

- Lock the door.
- Use heavy furniture to blockade the door.
- If the door has a hinge, use a belt to secure it.

Example of an easy way to secure a door. You can also use rope or a charging cord. Be innovative with everyday items. (Image Credit: pbs.twimg.com)

Take Action

Take action if the active shooter is nearby:

- Lock the door.
- Silence cell phones and/or pagers.
- Turn off any noise source (e.g., radios, televisions).
- Hide behind large items (e.g., cabinets, desks).
- Stay quiet.

If evacuation and hiding are not possible:

- Stay calm.
- Dial 911, if possible, to give police information on the active shooter's location.
- If you cannot speak, just leave the line open and allow the dispatcher to listen.

Fight

As your last resort, and only when in imminent danger, you can try to distract and/or incapacitate the active shooter by:

- Behaving as aggressively as possible towards him/her.
- Throwing items and improvising weapons.
- Yelling.
- Committing to your actions.

Basic First Aid

As part of preparing to be ready for any situation that gets thrown at us, we must talk about basic first aid skills. These skills are simple but could save your life or someone else's.

There was a teacher who was shot in the Columbine incident who died because of bleeding out. If someone had known to apply pressure to his gunshot wound, his chances of survival would have dramatically increased.

Gunshot Wound

A national awareness campaign—Stop the Bleed—was launched in October 2015 by the White House.[11] Stop the Bleed is a grassroots campaign aimed at educating and encouraging bystanders to help in a bleeding emergency until professional assistance arrives.

---

[11] "Stop the Bleed." Department of Homeland Security. July 26, 2018. https://www.dhs.gov/stopthebleed.

The campaign advocates the following steps in an emergency situation and is particularly relevant during an active shooter situation if someone near you suffers a gunshot wound.

Here are some tips for treating gunshot victims:[12]

Act quickly. Time is critical when treating gunshot wounds. Victims who reach medical facilities within the first hour after the shooting (called the "Golden Hour") have much better survival rates. Focus on moving swiftly and efficiently to treat the victim. Do your best to keep calm to avoid making the person feel more upset or panicked.

Apply direct pressure to control bleeding. Press bandages, gauze, or cloth directly on the wound, creating pressure with the palm of your hand. Hold for at least ten minutes. If the bleeding does not stop, examine the location of the wound and determine if re-positioning yourself or the bandage would help slow the bleeding. Always add new bandages over the old; do not remove bandages when they become soaked.

Apply a dressing. If the bleeding subsides, apply cloth or gauze to the wound. Wrap it around the wound to apply pressure. Do not, however, wrap so tightly that the victim loses circulation or feeling in their extremities.

If the bleeding doesn't stop, place a tourniquet 2–3 inches closer to the torso from the bleeding. Some common items that can be used in an emergency are belts, shoe strings, neckties, phone cords/chargers, clothing, socks tied together, rope, etc.

---

[12]   Strulovitch, Fran. "How to Treat a Bullet Wound." *WikiHow*, WikiHow, 1 Nov. 2018, www.wikihow.com/Treat-a-Bullet-Wound.

No matter how rapid the arrival of professional emergency responders, bystanders will always be first on the scene. A person who is bleeding can die from blood loss within five minutes, so it's important to quickly stop the blood loss.

Remember to be aware of your surroundings and move yourself and the injured person to safety, if necessary.

Call 911.

Bystanders can take simple steps to keep the injured alive until appropriate medical care is available. Here are three actions that you can take to help save a life:

1. Apply Pressure with Hands

EXPOSE to find where the bleeding is coming from and apply FIRM, STEADY PRESSURE to the bleeding site with both hands if possible.

2. Apply Dressing and Press

EXPOSE to find where the bleeding is coming from and apply FIRM, STEADY PRESSURE to the bleeding site with bandages or clothing.

3. Apply Tourniquet(s)

If the bleeding doesn't stop, place a tourniquet 2-3 inches closer to the torso from the bleeding. The tourniquet may be applied and secured over clothing.

> If the bleeding still doesn't stop, place a second tourniquet closer to the torso from first tourniquet.

PULL the strap through the buckle, TWIST the rod tightly, CLIP and SECURE the rod with the clasp or the Velcro strap.

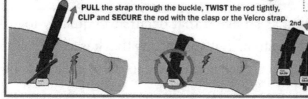

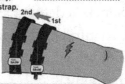

2nd ← 1st

The 'Stop the Bleed' campaign was initiated by a federal interagency workgroup convened by the National Security Council Staff, The White House. The purpose of the campaign is to build national resilience by better preparing the public to save lives by raising awareness of basic actions to stop life threatening bleeding following everyday emergencies and man-made and natural disasters. Advances made by military medicine and research in hemorrhage control during the wars in Afghanistan and Iraq have informed the work of this initiative which exemplifies translation of knowledge back to the homeland to the benefit of the general public. The Department of the Defense owns the 'Stop the Bleed' logo and phrase - trademark pending."

 Homeland Security

Office of Health Affairs

Be ready to treat the victim for shock. Gunshot wounds often cause shock, which is the body's response to trauma or loss of blood. This is extremely dangerous. Check to see if the victim's skin feels cool and try to regulate their body temperature by covering them with a coat or blanket. Loosen tight clothing.

Typically, you elevate the legs of someone experiencing shock. However, in this situation, evaluate the patient. Do not elevate the legs if they have a possible spinal injury or wound in the torso. Reassure the victim that help is on the way. Tell them that they're okay and that you're helping. Reassurance is important. Ask the person to talk to you.

Emotional Trauma

Immediately following an emotional shock, it's important to reassure the shocked individual. Keep sustained eye contact with them, make slow movements, and speak in a calm, slow voice.

Shock is defined as an event that occurs too quickly for "the human mind-body system." It is something that has overwhelmed the individual. Your presence and calm can help quiet and sooth the individual.

However, simply telling someone to calm down is ineffective. Lead by example. Give simple and specific advice in a gentle voice, such as: "Look at me and take a deep, slow breath … in and then out. Roll your shoulders … like this. Let your whole body go limp. … like this."[13]

---

[13]   Ibid.

Show how to perform each of these actions by doing them yourself. The shock victim may be unable to speak, but the ability to see and understand you may be intact. You want them to feel reassured and connected to you so that they can try to gain a sense of control over what's happening within their body.

Shocked individuals may shiver during or soon after the event (or sometimes hours or days later). The shaking is a natural, healthy response. It physically releases energy created by the shock. Let those body movements occur and assure the individual that this is natural.

At times, a shock victim may resist their rescuer. This occurs because the victim's mind-body alarm system is still in fight-or-flight mode. They are unable to stop themselves. As you try to help, know that they're not struggling against you (the helper); instead, they're struggling against the shocking event that's just occurred.

Cardiopulmonary Resuscitation (CPR)

In some instances, CPR might also be necessary. If a victim's heart or breathing has stopped, it's far better to do something than to do nothing; even if you're fearful that your knowledge or abilities aren't at 100 percent. Remember, the difference between doing something and doing nothing could be someone's life.

Here's advice from the American Heart Association: if you're not trained in CPR, then provide only chest compressions. That means uninterrupted chest compressions of 100 to 120 a minute until paramedics arrive. You don't need to try rescue breathing. If you do know CPR, just remember it's a 30:2 ratio of compressions to rescue breaths. If you are not formally trained in CPR, you should definitely consider taking the time to get the training.

Chapter 11

How to be a Hostage

In today's unpredictable environment, you really can't be overprepared. Situations can change in a flash, and as a consequence, you need to be resilient and quick thinking. Hostage situations may seem a distant threat, but they do occur. Sometimes it happens because the bad guys' plan doesn't go off as expected so they panic and take hostages. In other situations, hostages are the primary objective, typically as part of a kidnapping.

There are different motives for taking people—political beliefs, religious ideologies, or money. Captors use their hostages to gain an audience (usually in the media,) where they can espouse their message and beliefs. They often have demands and want to negotiate for something specific (e.g., policy changes, release of other individuals, etc.). Most hostages are used as negotiating tools to get something. In fact, in some parts of the world, kidnapping and ransoms have become a money-making industry.

As with every other situation we've discussed until now, remember there are tactics that you can arm yourself with to feel like you have options.

The first thing you must do is stay calm, especially at the beginning of the crisis. Anyone causing even the slightest additional chaos by panicking or acting out could find themselves eliminated (in a bad way). Stay calm with passive cooperation. There is a difference between being in a situation where hostages are taken unexpectedly and being a hostage as the result of a kidnapping.

In an unexpected hostage situation, the perpetrator didn't plan on taking hostages. They have typically been forced into the situation by outside forces (police, bystanders, etc.) and don't generally have a plan in place. These situations tend to be static, and they typically keep the hostages in the same location. In these standoffs, the longer a hostage event lasts, the better the survival chances for the victims.

In contrast, planned hostage events often involve moving the hostages. In these situations, the longer an event lasts, the lower the chance of survival. However, remember, you are comparing hours and days (unplanned) to weeks and months (planned).

There are four stages to a "planned" hostage situation:

> **Capture:** The most perilous time. The hostage taker is likely to be experiencing a range of emotions that will make them dangerous—nervous, unsure, irrational, easily irritated etc. Even if a hostage remains passive, the hostage takers may resort to violence in order to show control. Perceived resistance could result in harm or death. Try to control your emotions. If possible, attempt to signal someone that you are being taken against your will. You are only valuable alive, so compliance will increase

your chances. The more time that passes, the better your chances are of being released alive.

Movement: Hostage takers will then move you to a safe area. They are likely to physically control you; expect to be physically restrained or bound. If possible, put your hands in front of you to be bound and try to track your location as you go. Focus on remembering as many details about your surroundings as possible. If blindfolded, note turns and sounds. You may be drugged. If drugs are administered, don't resist. Kidnappers sedate victims so that they are easier to handle. The drugs may help you get control of your emotions, which should be your immediate goal.

Internment: In this phase, hostage takers will try to keep control over you and the situation. There are some things you can do to improve your conditions and improve your survival skills:

* Try to create a rapport with your captors. Ask about family, a universal subject. Avoid politics but listen attentively to their point of view.

* Plan on a long stay, so figure out a way to keep track of time. Note details like noise levels, temperature changes, activity, etc.

* Manage your time by setting a schedule that includes housekeeping, exercise, and hygiene; be creative.

* Try to build relations with other captives and captors.

* Eat the food provided to maintain your strength.

* Keep your mind active. Meditate. Daydream. Recall childhood memories, design a house in your mind, make up poetry, etc.

* Note characteristics of your captors and your surroundings. These details may be valuable later.

Resolution: This could come in the form of an escape, a release, or a rescue.

Escape from your captors is an individual decision based on the information at hand. Make sure you are mentally and physically capable of an escape. Know your surroundings. Who might be outside the door? Where are you? Will you have to walk through miles of desert or jungle to get anywhere? Are there other threats that will be worse than your current situation?

Release by your captors is another possibility. They may choose to release you for any number of reasons. They may also force you to leave. If so, follow their instructions. Be cautious and safe. The release could be a trap; be sure you are completely secure before you let your guard down.

Rescue is almost as dangerous as an escape or release. If you're being rescued, stay away from doors and windows. Lie flat on the ground with your hands behind your head. The final moments of a hostage incident will be tense. If a rescue team is in action:

* Remain calm and stay out of the way.

* Make no sudden moves; you do not want to be mistaken for one of the bad guys and risk being shot.

Even in a voluntary release or surrender by the hostage-takers, tensions are high, and tempers are volatile. Specific instructions will be given to hostages, either by the captors or the police. Follow instructions explicitly. You may be asked to leave with your hands in the air. You may be searched by the rescue team. It's possible you'll receive rough treatment until you are identified, and the situation has settled down.

Chapter 12

Securing Your Home While Away

While it's important to keep yourself safe while traveling, it's equally important to make sure your home is secure while you're away. Thieves, like predators, are lazy and want an easy hit to make their goal of robbing you quick and minimally risky. Don't let your home be a target or make it easy for them.

Here are a few things to keep in mind before you travel:

- Invest in a home monitoring system. There are great options on the market now that allow you to monitor your house remotely.

- Keep up the maintenance—get someone to mow the lawn or shovel the snow so it appears someone is there.

- Have someone take out your trash.

- Ask someone to watch your house and come by to pick up flyers or packages.

- Put a stop on newspapers and mail if you aren't having someone watch the house and collect these items.

- Keep valuables put away and out of sight so that someone looking in the windows won't see these items.

- If you can't afford to invest in a safe, hide valuables in inconspicuous places like food boxes in the pantry or containers in the bathroom cabinets.

- Don't hide keys outside your home—experienced thieves know to look for these.

- Program light timers on various lights around the house to come on and off at different times.

- Disconnect your garage door opener. Some universal garage remotes will open any doors.

- Lock the door coming from the garage to the house and double check that all windows are locked.

- Install outside door sensors.

- Advertise your security system with stickers and signs.

- Notify your alarm company that you will be out of town.

- Keep your blinds in their normal position.

- Don't save your "HOME" address on your vehicle GPS. Thieves have been known to break into cars at the airport to get home addresses since they know you are not there.

- Don't post on social media while you're away.

Chapter 13

Human Trafficking

Twenty-seven million victims confirm that human trafficking is a problem we need to tackle. As a business traveler, you have a unique opportunity to do something. You can educate yourself and be observant.

The first step when battling human trafficking is learning to recognize potential victims. In doing so, you may help save a life. Not all indicators listed are present in every human trafficking situation, and the presence or absence of any of the indicators is not necessarily proof of human trafficking.

It's important to remember that the safety of the victim, as well as the public, is a top concern. Do not attempt to take any action on your own to confront a suspected trafficker or alert a victim to your suspicions. Report your observations directly to law enforcement. They are equipped to investigate suspected cases of human trafficking.

The following list was created by the Department of Homeland Security's Blue Campaign program, which collaborates with government, non-government, private, and law enforcement groups to combat human trafficking.[14] The list describes common signs that can help people recognize human trafficking situations:

- Does the person appear disconnected from family, friends, community organizations, or houses of worship?

- Has a child stopped attending school?

- Is the person disoriented or confused, or showing signs of mental or physical abuse?

- Does the person have bruises in various stages of healing?

- Is the person fearful, timid, or submissive?

- Does the person show signs of having been denied food, water, sleep, or medical care?

- Is the person in the company of someone to whom he or she defers? Or someone who seems to be in control of the situation, (e.g., where they go or who they talk to?)

- Does the person appear to be coached on what to say?

- Is the person they are with dressed very differently from them? Are they in very worn or dirty clothing and the other person is dressed professionally or wearing high-end clothing?

- Does the person have freedom of movement? Can the person freely leave or move about? Are there unreasonable security measures?

---

14   "Indicators of Human Trafficking." Department of Homeland Security. October 17, 2018. https://www.dhs.gov/blue-campaign/indicators-human-trafficking.

Human trafficking is a modern-day form of slavery. Victims of trafficking are exploited for commercial sex or labor purposes. Traffickers use force, fraud, or coercion to achieve exploitation. The key distinction between trafficking and smuggling lies in the individual's freedom of choice throughout the process.

Of the more than 27 million victims of human trafficking, it is estimated half of the victims are children, including in the United States. How does someone become a victim? There are multiple ways: outright kidnapping off the street, conned by a job opportunity, sold by family, etc. In Europe and Israel, trafficked women are sometimes known as Natashas, which is a common name in those countries.

It's common to ask, why in the world would these victims not run when they have the chance while they are being transported? We think, they are in an airport with lots of people they could approach for help, there is law enforcement present/visible, they have the cover of a crowd to run and hide amongst, etc. But put yourself in the shoes of the victim.

- They may not speak English (or the language of the country they are taken to) and are unfamiliar with the culture.

- They distrust outsiders, especially law enforcement, due to fear of jail.

- Some do not identify as victims; they often blame themselves for being coerced or even kidnapped.

- Although many victims have been beaten and/or raped, their current situation may still be better than where they came from.

- Fear of safety for their family in their home country. They are often threatened that if they try to run, their families will be killed.

Techniques traffickers use to enslave and/or control victims:

- Debt bondage—Convincing the victim that they owe the trafficker a financial debt for food, housing, or travel out of their home country that must be worked off
- Isolation from the public—Limiting contact with outsiders and making sure that any contact is monitored or superficial in nature
- Prohibiting contact with family members and members of their ethnic and religious community
- Confiscation of passports, visas, and/or identification documents
- Violence or threats of violence against victim and/or victim's family
- Telling victims that they will be imprisoned or deported for immigration violations if they contact authorities
- Control of the victim's money; holding it for "safekeeping"

Program the following number into your phone to report suspected human trafficking while you're traveling: 1-866-347-2434.

Chapter 14

A Near Miss

While writing this book, the following situation happened to a male colleague's wife. I intentionally asked him to document and detail exactly what happened as the situation was occurring.

He has since commented, "Your book *needs* to get out." So much of this story played out exactly as the subject matter experts I interviewed described. Throughout the story, note references that are made to things such as the "feelings" that were ignored, lax behavior at the hotel, and the inadequate distance that was kept between cars while in transition—these are all things that we can learn from.

Bad things can happen, but with preparation, you can be ready.

Abduction Attempt

On March 12, my wife, Tammy, was traveling in Guatemala as a part of a new facility training and implementation team for her company. She had been in the country for about one week when I received a call from her. She sounded calm but confused and described to me how her group had narrowly escaped an attempted abduction.

March 12th—Online Post Describing Attack

Not knowing what to do, I immediately started reaching out to anyone who might know about situations like this. I keep in touch with a group of army friends, some of whom are still on active duty, via an online forum, and I thought they might have some insight on the situation. Here was my post:

Calling on anyone who has knowledge of traveling in/out of Guatemala. My wife has been there for a week traveling with her company. She has been following all the standard security protocols, only traveling with security, no taxis, etc.

Today, a local manager asked her and a couple of other Americans to go to lunch (they have been cooped up every day since they arrived in-country). She lowered her guard, and things went south.

They were in heavy traffic, and the driver pulled to a stop behind a large pickup. Eight (yes ... EIGHT) motorcycles pulled along both sides of the car ... each of the riders had a pistol in their hand. They all spoke in very clear English... and demanded that [the passengers] open the car doors.

The motorcycle riders began trying to break the windows with their pistols ... one rider drove his motorcycle around to the front of the car (between the car my wife was in and a pickup truck in front of them). One of the guys actually was able to get the passenger (front) car door open.

Throughout this scene, the ladies were all screaming at the top of their lungs to close the door, as she [the front passenger] fought off the assailant trying to get into the car. She was able to pull her arm back into the car and with both hands, she began pulling the door closed and wound up slamming the assailant's arm in the door several times. This made the attacker even more angry. They never demanded purses, etc. They kept repeating (again, in perfect English) to "open the f*&%ing door." They wanted IN.

The driver's window was halfway open (unusual for the area). One rider was reaching into the driver's door trying to open it. The driver handed her cell phone to the guy. He took the cell phone but continued trying to get into the car—pulling on the handle and yelling at the driver to open it.

Another rider was trying to get into the driver's side rear door (where Tammy was) and was yelling at her to "open the f*&%ing door, b*$#&." He stopped hitting the window with his pistol momentarily and shot a round in the air.

The driver of the truck in front of their car saw what was happening and put his truck in reverse and hit the gas. He smashed the motorcyclist in front between his truck and their car—and then got on the gas and tore off (smoking the tires). The guy in the front of the car was in pretty bad shape ... things just went even further south.

The motorcyclists (having seen their buddy get smashed) started freaking out. The guy trying to get into Tammy's door and another rider from behind the car rode around to the front of the car to check on their buddy and began yelling at the other cyclists in very fast Spanish. They picked the smashed rider up off the ground and placed him on the back of one of the bikes. Seeing this confusion, the driver of the car turned her wheel, hit the gas, and ran over the now crushed motorcycle. The motorcyclists remounted their bikes, and the whole group tore away from the scene. The ladies went around the block and returned to their office parking lot. All the ladies are okay (three Americans and one Guatemalan local).

As you can imagine—I am super concerned. They returned to the office and reported everything. My wife's boss told her not to tell anyone at the US office, as she didn't want to freak everyone back in Indiana out. They told both the security team escorting them and the hotel. Both committed to increasing their security presence.

I want my wife to get on the next thing smoking north—back to the US (or anywhere, really, that is not Guatemala). This whole shitty incident was not reported to the police ... they said they "Don't do that here." For some reason, nobody else seems to be freaking out over this except me ... and now my wife.

Here are some things that I noted that have me especially concerned:

- *They were in heavy traffic ... and these eight guys were coordinated enough to know which car they were after. Hell, I can't organize eight dudes to do anything with that much coordination ... so this to me seemed planned and not at all random.*

- *They immediately began yelling in ENGLISH ... did I mention that this was in Guatemala City—in broad daylight? THEY KNEW THEY WERE AMERICAN— otherwise they would have been yelling in Spanish. They did not speak English with an accent—it was very clear.*

- *They weren't purse snatchers ... they had no interest in purses or jewelry ... only ... OPEN THE DOOR ... nothing else. Eight dudes don't snatch purses. Eight dudes knock off banks ... or worse.*

So ... here I am researching how the hell to get my wife back asap ... I am concerned that she was targeted ... and I know from experience traveling abroad that you are most vulnerable whenever you are in transition.

Am I freaking out for no reason, or do you guys think that they were targeted? Do you think it could have been some random purse snatchers (or maybe carjackers) and not some other darker issue? Guys... I need your help here.

Many of you have been to G-City or worse ... should I freak out or not? AND ... what in the hell do I do about it? I was thinking that I would need to contact the State Department ... but their website basically says that they can't do anything ... same goes for the US Embassy ...

Thoughts? Ideas? Any help is appreciated.

March 12th–Responses to Abduction Attempt

SO … my friends/acquaintances immediately started responding. Here are some of their responses:

- *Eric contact the State Department? Delete the question marks and replace with exclamation marks. Contact State immediately!*

- *Been there many times … my guess is they were trying to kidnap an American for ransom money. I'd have her on the next flight out and tell the company to *$#%! off.*

- *E, I don't think there is such a thing as an overreaction to an attempted coordinated armed abduction in a third world $*%&hole, violent country. Get on this … NOW!*

- *Dude, telling the local police would likely be a waste of time in a place that needs a security team for escort. The police have been known to help coordinate abductions in G-City … Wishes for her safe return. If you need anything—PM me … I'm here for ya!*

- *You are your wife's only advocate. Don't rely on her boss to do the right thing. He's already proven to be a $%*&head … get her home … then get her a new job.*

- *E, where was the security detail? Were they in another car? OH … NVM – I just read the full post. I'm making some calls … check your PM's for contact … stand by.*

- *Eric, get in contact with the RSO (regional security advisor at the embassy) immediately. They may provide an expeditor at the airport.*

- *Yo! The most likely scenario is that they were made by gang members at the airport when they arrived. They've likely been following and tracking to establish a baseline schedule … when she deviated from normal … they saw their chance … and tried taking it.*

- *Eric, Guatemala is dangerous. Motorcycle crew robberies in Central America are a "thing." One guy spots a target and texts his buddies. If they were targeted for abduction by a fully armed eight-man crew—they would have been abducted, regardless of smashed compadre. Driver would be dead, too. I think this was a robbery, IMO. I would still get on the next plane though. Big cities in Central America get real sketchy fast. You want to get straight out on your way to the countryside and straight to the airport on your way back in.*

March 12th—Taking Action

I immediately reached out to US Embassy and the State Department. Never actually spoke with anyone … but left about 12 messages for various departments.

Embassy Contact

I started to worry more when I received a personal message from a friend who just left a post at the embassy in Guatemala City—he said:

Eric, I just left my post in Guatemala City—that story fits the M-O for a planned grab. You have to know, Americans traveling in G-City are frequently targeted as most of them who work for large companies have hostage insurance. There've been several Americans since last fall ... some reported through State ... but many don't even go that far ... they go through negotiators for the insurance companies. I have friends you need to talk to who I used at the Embassy for private security. Expect calls ... you need to answer them all ... Give me a half-hour to have someone in touch with you. In the meantime—call the RSO. His cell number is ###-###-####. Keep the pressure on State ... just make sure you don't sound like some kind of whack-job ... keep your powder cool when you talk to those guys ... they can be a real asset ... or a real ass ... It's up to you.

American Military Contractor

A short while later, I received a message from an American military contractor doing business in Guatemala City for executive travel, who has completed hostage negotiations on behalf of a few US companies. His message was bleak; he said that, as he understands it, "Somebody in the Guatemala office where your wife is working leaked their itinerary and is in contact with the baddies."

He went on to say that he believed that somebody with knowledge of her (and the team's) movements in enough detail to coordinate actions was sending real-time information to the abductors. Later in the message, he commented that he believes that they are watching for her (and the rest of the American team) to leave the office so they can make another attempt. He advised to contact the RSO at the US Embassy and make sure he knows that the whole American team at [Company X] was compromised and need to leave the country ASAP. He sent contact info for the RSO:

7-01, Zona 10
Guatemala City, Guatemala
Phone: (###) ####-####
Fax: (###) ####-####

Leaving the Office

Later, I got in touch with my wife to inquire what the security team was going to do … they decided to break up the American team and send them in multiple vehicles all driving in different directions. That way, if the attackers were to make another attempt – they would stand much less of a chance of abducting the whole team.

Additional Responses

In the meantime, one of my friends posted the following message for the group that was advising me:

E – Contact XXX Consultants. They are US based and are the best in the business. There's certainly no shortage of work down there… so I imagine they are even better now than they were when I was there (three years ago). I just texted their president— he'll be expecting your call. His private cell is (###) ###-#### (keep it that way, please).

I also received a note from a South African private security group doing business near Guatemala City.

You have to know that they were tipped off by someone who has been observing them or by someone who has been "helping" them. This is normal. The police are often in on it (not sure elsewhere in C-America—but at least in G-City) because 3rd world country, very low pay. Police will often take bribes to provide intel for some of these gangs that kidnap, then ask for ransom.

The main thing is that they want money, not hurt Americans. This is why they didn't fire into the vehicle. Guys speaking English without accents have grown up watching dozens of bootleg DVDs in English of Hollywood movies, are often ex-Army that attended training with US or have lived in the US or learned English in some kind of school, orphanage, etc.

Her company is half-stepping if they haven't hired more professional security consultants with the appropriate background to do this kind of work (CIA and State Department suck most of the time, so that isn't a resume enhancer usually). British, South African, French and US SOF communities are much better for this kind of work in general, with added filters to each one of those generalizations. (Young guy with SF background less experienced than older retiree with multiple plainclothes experiences in the region in question). Brits and French have a lot of experience in Central America, as do we.

Guys that are used to blending in—building rapport with locals, learning the gears of the area, who have contacts with key people in the area are better than some smooth talking blatantly-American who sticks out like a sore thumb. Our guys travel heavy (licensed in Guatemala) and have experience to get her out of country quickly. I'll need to coordinate with State Department if you want us to move forward. We already know much about the situation as there are several locals talking about it.

One of my friends referred me to someone they know at the embassy. Again, he advised speaking with the RSO—often the highest-ranking American security officer and the position has a lot of pull locally and with regional governments). He referred me to the RSO's cell phone and advised that if I don't get ahold of the RSO immediately, I need to contact the Marine Guard at Post 1.

March 12th – Evening in Guatemala

That night, my wife's security detail was able to get everyone to the hotel safely. However, we still were concerned that they were being watched and that their movement was being conveyed to others. I advised my wife to lock the door, to move furniture in front of the door, and to drive any wedges she could muster into the doorjamb. Expect no visitors … no room service, close the drapes, and keep volume of TV down low. It was a long night.

Kevin

On the evening of March 12, another one of my friends reached out to me. He is an ex-Army (Delta) Ranger who had a job with the government, but to this day, I don't know doing what … He works with various embassies in a lot of dangerous countries—I'll call him Kevin. His note follows:

Hey buddy ... long time no hear from ... just busting your balls, bro. I saw the post earlier ... I forgot ... I actually still do have contacts in Guatemala, a few who have been kidnapped before. If you have any security concerns in G-City—call me at ###-###-####, no matter the time (yes, even at 3 AM!).

Another resource would be the ### Church of Guatemala, it's a diverse English-speaking church that, due to the nature/diversity of the crowd, has a lot of experience helping Americans with security issues or who have been victims. Good luck ... make sure you call me!

March 13th—Plan

Trent

Bright and early on the morning of the 13th, I received a note from another resource. One of my friends made an introduction to this guy, who I will call Trent. He texted me with the following message:

Eric – I've been briefed on your wife's situation. Not to worry ... I can help. I am literally heading to the US Embassy in the next couple minutes. If needed, I can speak in person with the RSO. However, I need to hear from you in the next couple minutes. Once I leave my hotel, I won't be reachable on WhatsApp or iMessage and can only receive phone calls on my work cell.

That will work for the ten-minute walk to the Embassy, but I can't take my phone with me into the SCIF [Secure Compartmentalized Information Facility] or other secure areas where I work, so I'll be unreachable after that.

If you would like me to attempt to assist, I need to hear from you ASAP. (###) ###-#### is my work cell number. You can dial it as a normal American number, and it will ring down here. My WhatsApp info: (###) ###-#### is my stateside personal number. I don't have it activated on the local cell network, so don't call it directly. However, if you use that contact info in WhatsApp, you can text/call from within the app and get a hold of me. Personal email is: aaaaa@gmail.com is my Apple ID. You can send an iMessage and/or FaceTime with me. Personal email is preferred.

My work email is aaa.mil@###.com. I can check ID from the hotel (and obviously from work), but I don't get instant notifications. I suggest you get WhatsApp RFN as there are some things I need to discuss with you that should be secure. Tell Tammy to do the same … also, let her know I'll be texting her shortly.

At this point, I hadn't told him my wife's name … neither had my friend who made the introduction—and in no communication did I give my wife's cell number … So, I was starting to get a bit creeped out. (I was way too stressed out to go down that rabbit hole at the time. Although now, I look back on the situation and really am amazed at how much information they had. In a way I was grateful that they had it … but still … wow!

Of course, I downloaded WhatsApp immediately. Tammy already had WhatsApp, and Trent reached out to her:

Tammy, I spoke to your husband Eric about the incident in Guat City. I work out of the US Embassy and will be heading to work in the next couple minutes. I will be speaking to the RSO (security chief at the Embassy) but wanted to get a few more details." —Trent

I reached out to Tammy to tell her to expect texts and calls from Trent and advised he is one of the good guys … He reached out to her (and freaked her out a bit) … She was able to give him more details about her immediate situation. He relayed everything to the RSO, and together, they made some plans to get her moved from her hotel.

Later, Tammy received a couple texts from the RSO at the Embassy asking her to call him. He was concerned about the situation and its implications to security level of the region. If an abduction was confirmed, he indicated that the State Department would go to the highest security level and restrict all US travel to the region. (At this point, the State Department had a warning against travel to the area for all US citizens).

Tammy spoke with him further. At the time of this incident, the only other place where the State Department issued a higher security restriction was Afghanistan. She confirmed that the abduction was not successful, but that she was really concerned about the team's safety. They said that they were looking for more information about the abduction attempt through their own channels and would update her when or if they found anything out.

That afternoon, the American team was being moved to a hotel, all using different vehicles. Tammy was unfamiliar with the guard that was her escort that afternoon. She refused to get into the vehicle until she saw credentials and knew that he was her assigned guard. Once underway, she texted me from WhatsApp saying that she was still uncomfortable with the guard since she had never seen him before. All along the way, Tammy was texting me the names of cross streets as I was checking them off on a map of Guatemala City I had pulled up on my computer. I wanted to make sure that he was taking a fairly direct route to the hotel—and any deviation would be a sign that things were wrong.

At one point, the car stopped at a red light, and she immediately noticed motorcycles were coming alongside the car in between lanes. It was the same guys from the incident ... this time, they went around the car to the front and opened their visors and turned around and stared into the car as if to send a message that they were watching. Tammy took a picture of the motorcyclists and texted it to me (just in case).

She had with her a novelty souvenir knife that she purchased. I texted her back to place the knife in her hand and grip it very tightly—and if the driver looked like he was in on another abduction attempt, for her to drive the blade into his neck (she was seated directly behind the driver) as hard as she could. She agreed and waited for movement. The light turned green, the cyclists left the area, and the vehicle returned to the hotel.

March 13th—Evening

That night, Tammy was doing some reflecting on everything that her team should have done differently before the first incident.

- The first, and most obvious, was to not go out without security or in a personal vehicle.

- The other woman in the back seat didn't make copies of her documents to leave at the hotel. If she lost her purse in the attack, she wouldn't have had a passport or any other documents. Lesson: Put passports in the safe at the hotel. Carry a COPY of identification.

- The passenger in the front seat was wearing a very expensive diamond bracelet.

- Upon arrival, Tammy went to the hotel front desk to exchange cash (in $100 bills) for Quetzals (Guatemalan currency). She (and the others) did this not once, but several times. Several times, the hotel didn't have enough money, so they had to send someone to the local bank to be able to exchange the currency. Clearly, this could have marked the team.

- Tammy gave some of the local team access to her Facebook account. She also talked to them quite a bit about her life at home. She regrets connecting with some of them as she feels that it could have played a part in marking the team. Tammy's brother (who often posts on her Facebook page) is very wealthy. Someone reading some of the posts could interpret that even if the company didn't have ransom insurance, the family could clearly pay a ransom.

That night, one of the Marines from the Embassy—a friend of Trent's reached out to me (and, subsequently to Tammy) with an offer to have her (and others on the team) take his room as he and the other Marines were concerned for their safety.

Bill

In the meantime, I sent a note to some of my friends saying that I wished that I could kit-up and go there myself to get her out. Be careful what you wish for. That evening I received a note from "a friend of a friend." I'll call him "Bill." Bill sent me a WhatsApp message telling me the time that he was going to call and asking me to confirm that I wanted to go there (armed) to escort Tammy out.

The phone rang at the appropriate time, and he introduced himself. He asked, again, if I was serious. Of course, I said I was … at that point, I felt helpless and just wanted my wife out of there. Bill said he had posted something on my online forum asking for anyone else in our tight community who might be interested. He said he already had three confirmations of ex-SOF guys that volunteered to go with me—but that he was expecting more. He had to run but asked me to read his post—and the post of others—and to call him with an answer.

He had access to a (fast) plane that could accommodate up to 12 passengers. He said he frequented La Aurora Airport (Guatemala City) and could place a small group of people on the ground, but that he likely wouldn't be able to get anyone out of the City. The offer sounded too good to be true and very hard to believe. Later, I found the posting … and to my amazement … there were several people who volunteered to go with me to Guatemala to help my wife get out.

I copied and pasted the posting … but on second thought … it's probably best I not put it out there… The gist is that he was looking for combat vets only to volunteer to help out a fellow vet. I'll leave the rest of the details to your imagination ... Yeah ... it was that spooky. In all, there were well over 12 members willing to take an armed, unsanctioned trip into Guatemala to help my wife get to the airport, so she could return to the US.

I received another note from a friend saying to *"Be extremely cautious with exfilling (getting my wife out) the wife. Been there, done that ... the trip to the airport from Zone 10 (assuming that's where she's staying) is way more vulnerable than anywhere else ... Bad guys usu do more grabs in Zone 13 on the way to the airport. If they are watching her ... they will post up there—guaranteed. Talk to the RSO or PM me and I can put you in touch with some locals that are carded and are equipped for this stuff."* This message didn't do anything for my stress.

March 13th—Evacuation

In the meantime, Tammy's security team expanded and was now openly carrying long rifles in addition to the pistols they kept under their jackets. They wanted everyone to see that they were (heavily) armed. They also changed all travel routes and used multiple vehicles for any/all movement. My wife did not order anything to be delivered to her room, did not eat at the hotel restaurants, and stayed locked in her room until a plan could be made to get her (and her coworkers) to the airport.

Flight plans were made, tickets issued, and a plan was hatched to get the team to the airport. The hotel volunteered their whole security department to secure the outside of the hotel with (heavily) armed guards up and down the street. Movement to the airport was at 3:00 a.m., when traffic was light, ensuring wide open streets in case something bad happened. Private security arranged for three vehicles to escort the team to the airport, augmented by Trent and some of the Marines from guard post one at the embassy—all heavily armed.

The American team was escorted from their room by several Marines (plain clothes, but heavily armed). They were swiftly escorted from the door to the vehicles—and all vehicles left at once following very closely. Vehicles stopped at red lights with one car length in between the cars in case they needed to maneuver. When lights turned green, the cars resumed following very closely (within 2 feet from one bumper to another). Guards surrounded the American team all the way into the airport (while others brought in bags). Once in the secure zone, they were rushed to the plane and loaded straightaway.

Tammy landed two-and-a-half hours later in Houston … and then it all hit her … she finally was able to have emotions about things. She said she was never (ever) happier to be in the US in her life. This event changed her (and my) life forever. She learned many things to not do when traveling in high-risk areas. Thankfully, she lived through it and can pass her story on to others so that they might be able to avoid similar situations.

Travel Advisories

For reference, below is the State Department's Guatemala City travel advisory level during the time of the attempted abduction. For current travel information and advisories worldwide, go to Travel.State.gov.

Guatemala Department- Level 3: Reconsider Travel

Violent crime, such as armed robbery and murder, is common. Gang activity, such as extortion, violent street crime, and narcotics trafficking, is widespread. Local police may lack the resources to respond effectively to serious criminal incidents.

The following zones are of particular concern in Guatemala City due to crime: 5, 6, 7, 12, 13, 17, 18, 19, 21, and 24. Guatemala International Airport is located in Zone 13. Take appropriate security measures when traveling to and from the airport.

Do not hail taxis on the street in Guatemala City. Use radio-dispatched taxis (Taxi Amarillo), INGUAT approved taxis from the "SAFE" stand from the airport or hotel taxis.

Avoid areas outside of major roads and highways in the Guatemala Department and listed zones in Guatemala City.

Chapter 15

Gender and Vigilance

I wanted to share a final note that illustrates why it's so important—for women, in particular—to plan for their own safety. While writing this book, I came across Jackson Katz's book *The Macho Paradox: Why Some Men Hurt Women and How All Men Can Help*.[15] After reading through it, I noticed a lot of parallels between his study and the topic of vigilance. Rest assured that the work you're doing to keep yourself safe will surely extend to other areas of your life. See what you think.

Katz is a well-known social researcher whose work shows men why women are so pissed off, something even guys with wives and daughters sometimes don't get. What men don't understand, or experience, is the cumulative build-up of catcalls, unwanted advances, getting looked up and down, etc.

When giving talks, Katz conducts an exercise meant to help the men in the room get an idea of how women have to think as they go about their day.

---

[15]   Katz, Jackson. *The Macho Paradox: Why Some Men Hurt Women and How All Men Can Help*. Naperville, IL: Sourcebooks, 2006.

He draws and line down the middle of a whiteboard, and labels one side with the male symbol and the other side the female symbol, then asks men "What steps do you guys take on a daily basis to prevent yourself from being sexually assaulted?" He says usually there is a long period of silence, a few nervous laughs, and a few flippant comments. Eventually, someone speaks the truth and says they do nothing because they don't think about it.

He then asks the women the same question, "What steps do you take on a daily basis to prevent yourselves from being sexually assaulted?" Women start sounding off...

- Hold my keys as a potential weapon.
- Look in my backseat before getting in my car.
- Carry a cell phone.
- Don't go jogging at night.
- Make sure I see my drink being poured.
- Don't leave my drink unattended.
- Don't get on elevators with only one man.
- Vary my route home from work.

On average there are close to thirty things that women do—on a daily basis—to prevent themselves from being assaulted.

Let that sink in.

Thank You

Thank you for spending your valuable time reading this book and allowing me to share my passion and true desire to empower individuals with some simple tips and important information.

I hope you've discovered that you have more options than you previously thought to protect yourself. Continue to look for ways to innovate your safety by using the latest technology, with the goal of adding a layer, habit, or skill to your everyday vigilance.

Model and share your vigilance practices with your loved ones. Perhaps start by passing this book along to someone to read to improve their vigilance habits.

Please stay connected with me on social media to share your experiences, provide feedback, let me know what you think is important, and get more information and resources for yourself.

Sincerely,
Shelley Klingerman

Website: StilettoAgency.com
Email: shelley@stilettoagency.com
Facebook: /StilettoAgency
Twitter: @stilettoagency

About the Author

Shelley Klingerman is a successful entrepreneur, marketing professional, and documentary film producer. She is a graduate of Indiana State University and the mother of three beautiful children. It was because of these children she was inspired to produce the documentary film, *Terror in American Schools: Are Your Kids Safe?* The film outlines current threats to our schools, and what can be done to increase school security.

During her research for the film, and from her experience working for a large global firm for 18 years, Shelley began to understand the need to be vigilant and aware of her surroundings. This sparked a passion to help others learn what they should be aware of when traveling, walking alone, etc., and how they can prepare and protect themselves.

Shelley is currently the executive director of Launch Terre Haute, a nonprofit business incubator that helps entrepreneurs bring their business ideas to fruition. She currently resides in Terre Haute, Indiana, with her family.

Shelley is available for speaking engagements, workshops, and experiential learning programs (where she partners with law enforcement and military trainers to deliver an immersive experience).

Contact her at request@StilettoAgency.com to discuss your next event.